THE STANDEDGE TUNNELS

THE
STANDEDGE
TUNNELS

TREVOR ELLIS

Published by:

Huddersfield Canal Society
Transhipment Warehouse
Wool Road
Dobcross
Oldham
OL3 5QR

© Huddersfield Canal Society 2017

ISBN 978-1-5272-1554-2

Printed by: Chapel Press
                 Stockport

CONTENTS

Acknowledgements iv

Foreword v

Introduction vi

1   The Building of the Canal Tunnel (1793 - 1811) 1

2   The Operation of the Canal Tunnel (1811 - 1843) 27

3   The First Railway Tunnel - The Nicholson Tunnel (1843 - 1865) 37

4   The Second Railway Tunnel - The Nelson Tunnel (1865 - 1890) 47

5   The Third Railway Tunnel - The North Tunnel (1890 - 1894) 55

6   Standedge Tunnel, the Tunnel Book and After (1894 to Date) 67

Annexes

Annex 1 Developments at Tunnel End, Marsden 81

Annex 2 Developments at Diggle 97

Annex 3 Lengths of the Tunnels 105

Annex 4 The Shafts 109

Annex 5 Methods 121

Cover Illustrations:

Front -   Natural rock section in the Canal Tunnel. *Nathan Reynolds*
         A Manchester train emerging from the North tunnel at Diggle. *Trevor Ellis*
         Detail of the Nicholson and Nelson tunnels at Tunnel End (inset). *G. Westerby Collection*
Back -   A view of the Railway and Canal portals at Tunnel End. *Bob Gough*

Acknowledgements

I am indebted to the Huddersfield Canal Society for their support, not only financially but also by providing the services of their Administrator, Dr Bob Gough. I thank Bob in particular for his assistance in reviewing the work, laying out the book for printing and providing a full transcription of the Canal Company Minutes.

I appreciate the help I have had from various Archives, including those at West Yorkshire, The John Goodchild Collection and Ashton Local Studies. It is a real asset that much material is available online, particularly the Newspaper Archive and imagery from Google Earth®.

I would also like to thank several members of the Huddersfield Canal Society for their comments.

Foreword

In the 1970s, my wife and I somehow got involved in the newly-formed Huddersfield Canal Society, and explored the 'Narrow' Canal up to the entrance of the Standedge Tunnel, through the length of which we finally got to travel while filming the TV programme Great Canal Journeys about forty years later.

The history of this canal excavation, as well as that of the three successive railway tunnels alongside is full of the usual moments of optimism followed almost immediately by periods of doubt and uncertainty. The achievements of our great nineteenth-century engineering pathfinders have often only become possible through feats of low-key financial trafficking, share-holding pledges and shrouded boardroom manipulation, and Trevor Ellis has been into all this very thoroughly in his excellent book.

The eventual canal reopening was very well chronicled by the media, but I don't remember much attention being paid to the three railway tunnels, each of whom has its own story to tell. Tunnelling has, of course, always been a perilous occupation, and I think it is hard for us today to accept that less than a hundred years ago large groups of 'navvies' were prepared to work (and not infrequently die) on projects like these punitive excavations, portrayed at the time as crucial and then abandoned a few years later because of increases in the rates.

Such stories are deeply woven into our history, and I was grateful to have been given the chance to unpick a little more about the Standedge Tunnels.

Timothy West
November 2017

Introduction

I joined the Huddersfield Canal Society in 1976, two years after its formation. At the time there were still fresh memories of the trips which had been organised into Standedge Tunnel in the 1960s, and before, and a key aim of the Society was to re-establish these. The British Waterways Board (BWB), as they were at that time, seemed to be afflicted with the same disease that affected the railways and a number of other industries which were presiding over their own slow demise and they seemed, for the most part, to view us as an irritation. Our efforts only served to create an atmosphere of secrecy.

Around 1984 I recall attending a meeting where Geoff Brown, a member of the Canal Society and also of the local Railway Circle, gave a presentation on Standedge Tunnel. I was particularly impressed by his statement that he was writing a book on the tunnels and his credibility was greatly enhanced by the presence, at the back of the meeting, of Malcolm Stakes, then the BWB's Principal Mining Engineer, who had travelled from a distance to hear Geoff speak.

The restoration of the Canal started with work on the Uppermill length in the 1970's, followed by a number of projects using Community Programme funding in the 1980's, which brought the Local Authorities on board and led to the launching of the Huddersfield Canal Joint Committee, which involved all of the partners, including the Society, through its subsidiary, HCS Restoration Ltd. In this way, the restoration started to make real progress and by the late 1990's only the Tunnel and the major blockages in the centre of Stalybridge and through Huddersfield remained. This led to the awarding of Millenium Funding and the re-opening of the Canal in 2001.

Recalling Geoff saying he was writing a book on the tunnels, I took the opportunity of the re-opening to ask how his book was going and whether the Society could publish it as part of the celebrations. He declined. When Geoff died, his wife Kath approached me to offer his research to the Society in the hope that someone could complete the work. Two trips were necessary, filling my car to the maximum. However, I could find only the text of what would have made a fairly basic booklet, rather than a book, and no trace of the 'resumé' which was referred to in some of his correspondence. I did find one letter in which he appeared to be discouraged by the fact that others had published works, presumably Graham Keevil with his "Standedge Guide" and the various works of Professor R B Schofield. Although I had been involved in a lot of historical research into the Canal with Keith Gibson, for his books, and with Dr Bob Gough, at the time I considered the task of starting from scratch on a book about the tunnels beyond me.

When the re-opened Tunnel was first used for transits, British Waterways (BW) were still very nervous of the Health and Safety implications and serious limitations were in place, with unoccupied boats being towed through in convoy. However, with experience of operation, it proved possible to relax some of the restrictions and boaters were allowed to take their own boats through the Tunnel, though accompanied by a member of BW staff.

With the formation of the Canal & River Trust in 2012, the emphasis moved to using volunteers and, in 2016, I started to volunteer as a Boat Chaperone, accompanying private boaters through the Canal Tunnel. From my observations, I became concerned that some of the previous publications contained inaccuracies and that none covered all the tunnels and their surroundings as a whole. I also felt that much new research and some unpublished parts of Geoff's work ought to be made available.

I hope that this book adds a little to the sum of knowledge on the subject. Inevitably there will be some inaccuracies, but I trust that these will serve to inspire others to look further into the history.

Trevor Ellis
Huddersfield

Figure 1 - The George Inn originally stood at the end of the Market Place in Huddersfield - it was demolished in 1851 to create John William Street for access to the railway station.

1
The Building of the Canal Tunnel 1793 - 1811

The proposal for *"An Intended Canal from Huddersfield to join the Canal from Manchester to Ashton-under-Lyne"* was launched at *"a numerous and respectable meeting at the House of Humphrey Dyson in Marsden"* on 17th May 1793, chaired by John Plowes, a Leeds Merchant who also had interests in the village. The meeting was reported in advertisements in the Manchester Mercury and the Leeds Intelligencer, which announced a second meeting to be held at the George Inn in Huddersfield on 31st May when subscriptions for shares would be taken. Those subscribing for shares were known at the time as 'Proprietors'. In the event, £150,000 of the £200,000 specified as the cost of building the canal was promised immediately, though, in the practice of the time, it was only necessary for subscribers to put down the first £1 or £2 on each £100 share. This situation would cause the Huddersfield Canal Company serious problems as time went on.

Figure 2 - The façade of the George Inn was re-erected by Messrs Parkin of Huddersfield and Castlehill at St Peters Street, Huddersfield and recently commemorated by the Huddersfield Canal Society with the fixing of a plaque to the façade. (Inset - Bob Gough)

The year 1793 was the height of what became known as the 'Canal Mania' and William Pontey, a Landscape Gardener and Seedsman from Huddersfield, who later wrote a highly critical account of the Canal, suggested that speculation was the motivation of many of those attending.[1] He described a scene where people rushed to buy shares and even encouraged others to buy on their behalf so that they could avoid what he says was the limit of 5 shares per subscriber, in the hope of selling at a profit. (Pontey himself seems to have owned 6, as did numerous others, so he may be mistaken and 6 may have been the limit.) His version is difficult to verify as the first listing of Proprietors available is that in the Act of Parliament, which appears to consist mainly of local people. However, many of the speculators may have moved on quickly, having sold their shares. Although apparently criticising the activity, Pontey himself went on to sell his own shares, though he later acquired another and remained a Proprietor and active participant for some years.

By 23rd October 1793, when a meeting of those who had become Proprietors was held at the George Inn in Huddersfield, Benjamin Outram, who had carried out the initial survey, had been appointed to be the Engineer of their canal and Nicholas Brown its Surveyor. Outram was an up and coming canal engineer, but Brown was a local man, from Saddleworth. Brown was probably known to several of the main Proprietors, but his experience of such work would be limited at best to the setting out of the dams and goits of the local water-powered mills and this is probably the most that any of the Proprietors would have seen of the kind of engineering works that were proposed. Outram, as the Chief Engineer, was paid at a rate of 3 guineas (£3 3s or £3.15 in modern money) per day, but was probably only required to attend for a few days each month and for Committee meetings as required, so much of the day-to-day work would fall on the relatively inexperienced Brown.

---

[1] *Pontey, W., (c.1811). A Short Account of the Huddersfield Canal (Cambridge). It was aimed at deterring potential speculators in a proposed London and Cambridge Canal.*

Outram recommended a line *"to commence at Sir John Ramsden's Canal near Kings Mill in Huddersfield and to pursue the valley to Waterside in Marsden, there to enter the hill and to proceed via a tunnel three miles in length under Peele-moss and Brun-top, to Broadbent's Mill in Brunn-clough, where it will excavate; then pursue the valley, and passing thro' the hill opposite Scout Mill by a tunnel 200 yards in length, by Staley Bridge to the Ashton-under-line canal."* He described this route as *"in every respect practicable,"* going on to say that *"the hill through which the Tunnel is to be made appears favourable, the strata consists of gritstone and strong shale, and the low ground in the center near Red-Brook will afford an opportunity of opening the works by means of steam engines, so as to greatly facilitate the completion of the Tunnel, which I conceive may be accomplished in five years."* He did concede that *"the lockage and tunnel, unavoidable from the nature of the hills which intersect the country make the expence.... very considerable."* He put a figure of £164,948 on the cost of the canal, with a further £13,800 for reservoirs bringing the total to £178,748. £4,000 was subsequently added for additional reservoir capacity to placate the local mill owners, who were concerned about the canal taking the water that powered their mills. Outram, with the assistance of Brown, prepared the necessary

ANNO TRICESIMO QUARTO

Georgii III. Regis.

C A P. LIII.

An Act for making and maintaining a Navigable Canal from and out of the Canal of Sir *John Ramsden* Baronet, at or near the Town of *Huddersfield*, in the West Riding of the County of *York*, to join and communicate with the Canal Navigation from *Manchester* to or near *Ashton under Lyne* and *Oldham*, at or near the Town of *Ashton under Lyne* aforesaid, in the County Palatine of *Lancaster*.

[4th *April* 1794.]

WHEREAS the making and maintaining of a Canal for the Navigation of Boats, Barges, and other Vessels, from and out of the Canal of Sir *John Ramsden* Baronet, at a certain Place between the *King's Mill* and the Town of *Huddersfield*, in the West Riding of the County of *York*, to join and communicate with the Canal Navigation from *Manchester* to or near *Ashton under Lyne* and *Oldham*, in the County Palatine of *Lancaster*, at a certain Highway in the Town of *Ashton under Lyne* aforesaid, near and leading to a Bridge called *Dukinfield* Bridge, in the County Palatine of *Chester*, will be of great publick Utility, will open a useful, short, and easy Communication between the Towns of *Man-*

9 F 2   7   *chester*

Figure 3 - The first page of the Act of Parliament for the building of the canal.

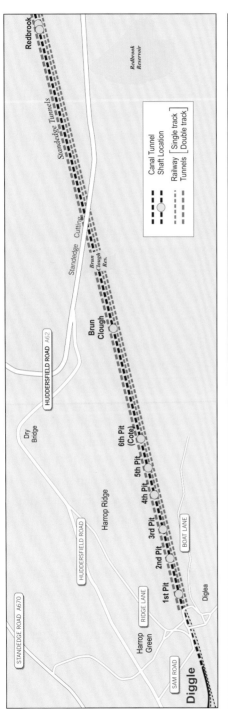
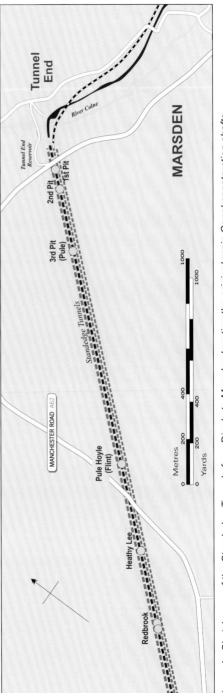

Figure 4 - Sketch map of the Standedge Tunnels from Diggle to Marsden locating the original main Canal construction shafts.

documentation to apply for an Act of Parliament, during which another increase in the capacity of the reservoirs took the total cost to £182,748, of which the Tunnel was estimated at £55,187. The Act received the approval of Parliament on 4 April 1794 and a Committee of the principal Proprietors (it was necessary to hold 5 shares or have paid at least £100 to be on the Committee) was formed. At its second meeting on 11th July 1794, the Committee resolved to let a contract for the digging of 1,000 yd at the western end of the Tunnel to Thomas Lee, subject to Outram's agreement, and they sent Outram a message that they wished to proceed with the work on the Tunnel as a matter of urgency. At the next meeting on 4th September they ordered the Company Secretary to affix the Company Seal to the contract.
That this was the early days of the Company is illustrated by the fact that the very next item minuted is to obtain a Company Seal.

On 29th June 1795, the Committee appointed a John Evans to supervise the Tunnel works at a salary of 2 guineas per week. They were also carrying out experiments to find the best coal for the steam engines, which were erected at the various shaft sites. (Work was presumably going on using directly employed labour in addition to Lee.)
On the 1st September 1796 they agreed to let a contract to a George Evans *"for cutting and making part of the Tunnel on the Line of the said Canal under Pule Moss and Brunn Top."* While this description appears to suggest a section somewhere within the central part of the Tunnel, none of the shafts in the central part had reached tunnel level by this date and from later Minutes it appears that George Evans was actually working the eastern end. The two Evans were possibly Welsh miners. *(For details of construction methods, see Annex 5)*

The first signs of impending problems appear at a meeting on 29th September 1796, when *"It having been represented to this Meeting that very considerable Sums of Money are expending in endeavouring to raise Water from and to sink some of the Pitts(sic) on the Line of the Tunnel without advancing with the Works in proportion equivalent to the Expences,"* it was *"Resolved that Mr Outram be desired immediately to attend to the above Representation and to take such steps as may appear to him most for the Interests of the Company and that he do report his Opinion on this Business at the next Committee Meeting.*" Ominously, at the same meeting there was a discussion about the action to be taken against Proprietors who were defaulting on the payments due on their shares.

Despite this resolution, the Minutes of 16th November 1796 make no mention of any report by Outram, though it was minuted that "*As from the Information of Mr Brown and Mr Evans* (presumably John) *it appears to this Committee that the Average Expence of working the Engine at the Pit called the sixth Pit in Diggle is eleven Guineas per Week exclusive of the Wear and Use of the Engine and that the Depth of sinking in each Week has been on an average one Yard and that the power of the Engine is inadequate to the Work. Resolved that the Works at the said Pit be suspended until Mr Outram shall have fully considered the propriety of the working at that Pit and shall direct the*

Figure 5 - Redbrook Engine House, taken by Geoff Brown in June 1959, prior to the demolition of the annexes at either end. The engine house at the far end would have contained the pumping engine, with some winding arrangement at the near end - note the blocked archway. (The brick construction in the photograph is later.)

recommencing of such Works." As this shaft was planned to be around 240 ft. deep, the Committee's concern about a sinking rate of 3 ft. per week is understandable. Certainly, eleven guineas (£11.55 in modern money) was a lot of money by the standards of the time when the salary of the man supervising the work was 2 guineas per week. It is clear that the work was eventually resumed on the 'sixth pit' as it is today's Cote Pit, the first shaft from the Diggle end which remains open. However, according to Geoff Brown's notes, this shaft may not have been completed until 1807 and it appears that the fourth and fifth pits from Diggle were never completed down to tunnel level. Given that the first six shafts were only on average 150 yd apart, it is possible that the digging of the Tunnel eventually proceeded faster than some of the shafts could be dug.

Coal remained a problem and at the meeting on 5th January 1797, after a trial, they agreed to try coal from Committee member George Woodhead's colliery. This was in Elland and the coal was to be delivered at Red Brook and Pule Hoyles, which would have necessitated hauling it up a number of severe gradients along the then turnpike road route over a distance of about 14 miles. The engines in use would be the primitive Newcomen type, which had a voracious appetite for coal. Such engines were often used to drain collieries, where their coal consumption was less of a problem, but on the moors above Marsden, their appetite for fuel would be a major concern.

Trevor Ellis

Figure 6 - The UK's last Newcomen Engine still on its original site at Elsecar Heritage Centre, Barnsley, West Yorkshire.

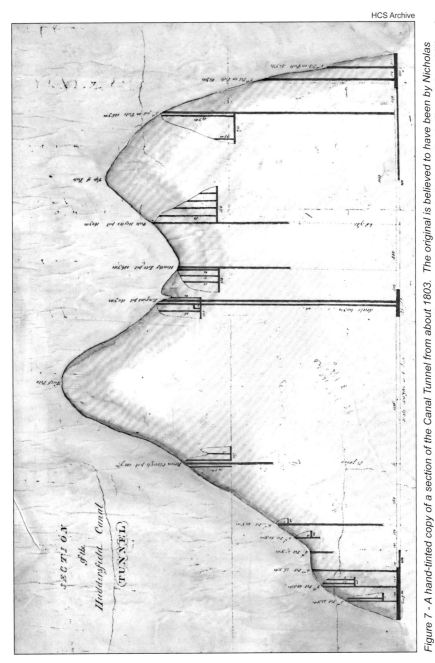

Figure 7 - A hand-tinted copy of a section of the Canal Tunnel from about 1803. The original is believed to have been by Nicholas Brown, the Surveyor, and later amended by his successor William Bayliffe. The section shows both the main shafts and the additional shafts and adits for drainage and the use of water engines. It illustrates clearly how little progress had been made on the tunnel itself.

Money problems became more serious and on 7th April 1797 the Committee decided to limit operations to only three of the shafts. These were the sixth Pit, where they had earlier suspended operations, the Engine Pit (Redbrook) and the Pit on Pule Hill. The first and the last of these were presumably needed to support the work proceeding at the two ends and Redbrook was near to the middle of the Tunnel, from where the Committee intended to work outwards in both directions. Restrictions were also placed on the expenditure which Nicholas Brown was permitted to make on other structures along the canal line. At their previous meeting also, there was a debate about *"the small engine"* which had been supplied by a Mr Smith of Chesterfield. There seems to have been a dispute about the suitability of the engine, which must have been partly justified as Smith had agreed to make modifications. They agreed to pay him two hundred pounds on account of the balance due, *"in six Weeks from this Day or sooner if the funds of the Company will admit thereof."*

Figure 8 - Remains of the top of Heathy Lee main shaft.

At its meeting on 8th June 1797, the Committee reversed its decision to suspend the works at Brun Clough and Flint or Pule Hoyles shafts after Outram warned them of the likely effect on progress. This is typical of the way in which the Committee members vacillated throughout the early years of the project. They still had no more money than they had when the decision to suspend the work had been made. At the same meeting it is mentioned that John Evans was taking on a contract to carry out part of the works, presumably instead of his supervisory role, though no details are given of which part of the Tunnel this was.

There must have been concern amongst some of the Proprietors, both about the chosen line and the standard of the work being done. At a meeting of the Proprietors, they resolved that *"a proper person shall be appointed to view the line of the....canal and the execution of the works thereof..."* In August 1797, the Committee received a report from the canal engineer Robert Whitworth Snr on the state of the canal.[2] Whitworth, in general, appeared to approve of the line, apart from around Slaithwaite, and of the workmanship, which is strange in light of later comments by John Sutcliffe, a minor canal engineer who later published a book in an effort to promote himself.[3] In it, he commented that *"The masonry and earth work of this canal were the worst executed of any I ever saw. This was the opinion of the late Mr. Whitworth, who was called in to survey the line, and said to me the work will be nearly all to do over again, particularly the locks."* Although Whitworth addressed his report to *"the Company of Proprietors of the Huddersfield Canal,"* it may be that he was trying to satisfy the Committee, or perhaps he was reluctant to criticise a fellow engineer, who could perhaps one day be employed to check his work. Some of the report does appear evasive, but on the question of the locks, for example, he stated *"The Plan they are built on is a very proper one for Strength and Permanency."* It may be that Sutcliffe was writing with the benefit of hindsight as, by the time that his book was published, it was known that most of the locks had needed to be rebuilt. On the question of Standedge Tunnel, Whitworth did say that *"It really is alarming to view the profile of this Tunnel and to see how little is*

---

[2]   *Text published in "Pennine Link," the Journal of the Huddersfield Canal Society, Issues 31 (Nov 1979) to 34 (May 1980). Original source unknown, but a Canal Company Minute states Whitworth was paid £21 for the report.*

[3]   *Sutcliffe, J. (1816) A Treatise on Canals and Reservoirs, Cotton Spinning, Corn Mills, Grinding, Preserving Grain, and Public Drains (Rochdale). The title gives some idea of the range of work expected of an engineer at the time.*

done, in Proportion of what is yet to do…", though even here he tried to minimise his comments by referring to the progress on digging the shafts and the availability of materials for future works.

Only a month later, the Committee were informed that Thomas Lee was unable to fulfil his contract *"having been impeded in the Execution of the Work by many unforeseen Circumstances."* Lee had apparently lost heavily on the contract and the Committee authorised an additional payment of up to fifty pounds. Three of their number were appointed as a sub-committee to inspect the works. Lee's problems were probably due to Outram's over-optimistic view of the strata, which he had considered would need no additional support or lining. This is confirmed to an extent as at their November meeting the Committee agreed to allow him an additional £300 for timber shoring that he had purchased and improved his terms by fifteen shillings a yard on the remainder of his contract, at the same time allowing him an extra year to complete. They were clearly in a difficult position and badly needed Lee to continue the work. However, even on the new terms he was unable to do so.

Matters deteriorated further by February 1798, when the Committee agreed *"to contract with Matthew Flint and his Partners for the Execution of that part of the East end of the Tunnel which George Evans has deserted."* Further efforts were in hand to raise additional funds. In April they resolved *"That Mr Outram be directed to make the best Agreement he can for carrying on the Works of the Tunnel from the Red Brook Engine until the further Directions of the Committee"* – this would appear to be a different problem to the George Evans one, though its exact nature is unclear from the Minute. In June the following year George Evans took legal action against the Company and the matter would drag on until late in 1801 before finally disappearing from the Minutes. It is quite possible that he too had taken on a contract on the basis that little or no lining or support would be needed. Another possibility is that, working from the eastern end, he had reached a fault which took him from the easier worked strata predicted by Outram into the sandstones and Millstone Grit. In either event, the basis of his case may thus have been that Outram's optimistic report about the geology had misled him when he agreed to the terms of his contract. William Pontey would later query, *"How did he (Outram) know what would be found in the Tunnel, though about 200 yards below the highest part of the Mountain?"*[1] Nothing is subsequently minuted about *"Matthew Flint and his Partners"* and it is not known whether they actually started work. However, Bob Gough has pointed out the possible link between the name and Flint Pit, which had earlier been known as Pule Hoyles. Other evidence is circumstantial. Nothing is minuted about them not starting work, whereas the failures of other contractors tended to be recorded at some length.

Figure 9 - Present day view of Flint Pit (old) with the remains of an associated engine house.

In August 1798 it was minuted that Outram had settled the account between the company and John Evans for excavating part of the Tunnel and it appears that the Committee agreed to cancel the balance of the contract. John Evans had taken on this contract in June 1797, but no details were specified at that time and nothing was now said about the consequences of the cancellation, so it is impossible to tell from the Minutes which part of the Tunnel he had been working on. With Lee and George Evans engaged at the two ends it could be that he was responsible for the short stretch which was dug at Redbrook in the middle of the Tunnel. Interestingly, a John Evans appears to have become a Proprietor and this man continued to attend meetings for some time, which might explain why this relationship remained harmonious and received Outram's personal attention.

In October 1798, the Company gave notice to Nicholas Brown and appointed William Bayliffe, who had previously been responsible for the west side of the canal to be Surveyor for the whole canal in his place. Brown would not disappear from the scene, but would in future have a lesser role under Bayliffe, whom he had previously been supervising.

It appears that the Company may have been running out of potential contractors as in February 1799 they asked Outram to prepare an estimate of the cost of completing the Tunnel on their behalf. Although nothing is said about work ceasing, they also minuted that their coal suppliers be notified that no more coal would be required until further notice. Work had probably ceased at Redbrook and it may be that they had now managed to convert their remaining operations to water power or were relying on gravity to drain the two ends where work was proceeding. It was minuted in March that Outram submitted an estimate, and this was to be referred to a Special Meeting of all the Subscribers. John Sutcliffe, in his book, commented *"£56,000 were estimated to finish the Tunnel; for that sum, it is said, the engineer offered to execute and find security to complete it, in five years; but some of the committee being of opinion, that it might be executed for less money, he fortunately was not the undertaker."* [3] It would appear that Sutcliffe may have thought that this offer had been made at the outset of the works. By the time that Outram actually put in the offer, Sutcliffe's reason for it not being accepted seems unlikely, given the difficulties that the Company was having with contractors and the fact that they had asked Outram to put in the estimate. At the same March meeting, the Committee agree to contract with William Davenport, a Marsden Innkeeper, to carry goods between their warehouse in Marsden and the one at Woolroad in Saddleworth.

Unfortunately, it was only shortly afterwards that the canal was seriously damaged by floods, and this may well be why nothing more was heard of either proposal, as the Company's financial concerns suddenly overwhelmed them. By this stage the Committee had called for the full £100 payable on each share, though there was a major problem of Proprietors who were unable to pay, or who had died. Only around 500 yd of tunnel were finished and around 1,200 yd of heading had been cut.[4] There are frequent references to shares being ordered to be forfeit for non-payment and being resold by the Company and it must have been clear that a serious amount of new money would be required both for repairs to flood damage and to complete the Tunnel.

There are a number of references in the Minutes to the damage caused by the floods, but it is not until a committee meeting in November 1800 that anything more is minuted about the Tunnel. The reason for this seems to be that the Company had been forced to apply for a second Act of Parliament to enable them to raise additional money to make repairs to the completed sections of the canal and to continue the Tunnel and that all work on the latter had ceased in the meantime.

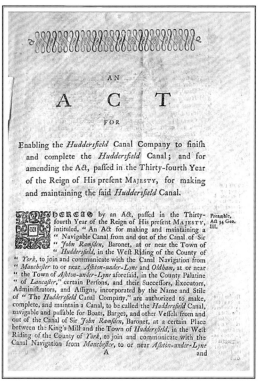

Figure 10 - The first page of the second Act of Parliament for completing the building of the canal.

---

[4]   Schofield, R.B., (2000). *Benjamin Outram, 1764-1805: An Engineering Biography (Merton Priory Press)*. Schofield quotes Malcolm Stakes, Principal Mining Engineer of British Waterways in the 1970s/80s.

A Special Meeting of the Proprietors in September 1799 had agreed that the new Act would be required to raise the sums needed to make repairs and to complete the canal. The Act was passed in the Spring of 1800 and allowed the Company to raise money by extra calls of up to £20 on the existing shares and to issue new shares. It would appear that the Proprietors were understandably now keen to take more control, as around this time the General Meetings start to Minute resolutions which they require the Committee to carry out.

It would be 1801 before the new shares could be issued, and the Summer of 1800 was occupied by repairs to make the canal navigable again. For the present, the Company were reliant on existing Proprietors paying the extra amount and would continue to be afflicted by the problem of those who were unwilling or unable to pay.
A General Meeting in October resolved that the Tunnel should be worked from the two ends, mainly on cost grounds. Two resolutions were minuted at the next Committee meeting in the November:

Firstly it was *"Resolved that Mr Outram be and he is hereby requested immediately to furnish the Committee with his opinion of the best mode of proceeding with the Tunnel at each end and the probable weekly expenditure of such mode and his reasons for forming his opinion to enable the Committee to state fully their opinion thereon to the general Meeting on the fifteenth day of January next."* This appears to confirm that no work has been going on in the Tunnel and that the Committee were looking to restart in a limited way.

Secondly it was *"Resolved that Mr Outram be also requested immediately to inform the Committee of the best line and mode of making a Railway over the Hill in order to convey Goods between Marsden and the west end of the Tunnel and the probable expence of such Railway."* This further suggests that the Committee now accepted that the Tunnel was unlikely to be finished for some considerable time and were in the meantime seeking an alternative that would enable them to trade and earn some money.

In February 1801, expenses were paid *"to Thomas Green, Thomas Jenkins and John Green ... John Varley of Shardlow ... John Thompson and Richard Hallos ... William Williams and John Prichard ... for their expences in coming over to Huddersfield respecting the undertaking the execution of the Works of the Tunnel."* As in the case of the earlier contractors, there are a number of Welsh names here. Soon afterwards the Committee were keen to take up the offer of John Varley. At the same time, William Bayliffe resigned as overall Surveyor. Although he is mentioned frequently in the Minutes, he does not appear in connection with work on the Tunnel, probably because little was happening during his time in the post. He continued to have a lesser role until 1803, when he finally disappears from the Minutes following a dispute about the building of the towpath bridge at Stalybridge aqueduct.

The issue of the new shares in 1801 is the cause of one of the complaints in William Pontey's pamphlet.[1] Due to the additional calls on the original shares, anyone holding those would by now have subscribed £120. However, anyone making a first payment on the new shares immediately had the same voting rights etc. at a price which Pontey gives as £8 13s.

In April 1801, John Rooth was appointed *"to superintend and manage the works of the Canal and the general Concerns of the Company."* Rooth was the nephew of William Rooth, one of the Directors, who was a Wakefield-based merchant and shipowner. As 'John Rooth and Company,' the '& Company' probably being his uncle, he had approached the Canal Company in December 1800 with proposals to become a carrier on the canal and to promote trade, which they had eagerly accepted. Unlike many of their appointments, this one was to prove reasonably successful. John Rooth had already started to supervise work on the canal in addition to his carrying business and would quickly become a man whom they relied on totally. Worryingly, at this meeting they directed him to examine the Levels of the Tunnel and *"to ascertain whether the parts begun are cut in the exact level and direction so as to correspond with the Levels of the Canal at each end of the Tunnel."* To enable him to do this, they also authorised the purchase of *"an Instrument of the best quality and construction for taking Levels,"* which does raise the question of how his predecessors had been managing up to that point.

At the very next meeting later in the month, the Committee hit a problem with John Varley, who had been on the verge of signing a contract for the Tunnel works. One of the men he named as being prepared to share with him in a bond of £5000 declined to put forward any money, although he did write to say that he had no doubt that Varley would complete the work! As appears typical of the Committee, instead of going back to their previous short list, a new name, a Mr Cartwright of Birmingham, was now their favourite for the job. At the June meeting they were hopeful of letting a contract and it was suggested that all members be present at the next meeting for this purpose. Instead, Cartwright is never mentioned again and there is a Minute to the effect that Varley had re-appeared with some different guarantors. However, these guarantors would need six years to pay in the event of any failure and Varley also wished to renegotiate the contract, so it was resolved to have nothing further to do with him. Notwithstanding this decision, Varley reappeared towards the end of a meeting in August, now prepared to work to the original contract and with his guarantors agreeing to the terms. As several Directors had already left, the matter was deferred to the next meeting, though those present were in favour of accepting his offer. On 7th August 1801 the Committee agreed to contract with Varley, presumably because they had few or no alternatives. Perhaps wisely, they also appointed a John Booth of Greenacres, who had already done some surveying of the Tunnel works, as Superintendent, and agreed to pay for him to have an assistant.

In October 1801, Varley's guarantors again refused to sign the Agreement and the Committee once more resolved to have nothing further to do with him. Around this time, though the matter is never minuted, Outram appears to have left the Company. The decision on Varley is the last Minute that refers to him. Faced with the demise of the Varley contract, and with no further contractors in view, the Committee decided to turn to John Rooth and their newly appointed supervisor, John Booth of Greenacres, and ask them to start work on the Tunnel from the two ends using directly employed labour.

In April 1802 the Committee asked Rooth to investigate the possibilities of using a spray of water down the Brun Clough shaft to ventilate the workings. This must have been successful as such an arrangement was in use at Redbrook until around the end of the steam railway era in the 1960s. The Company was also still trying to reach a final settlement with its former contractors George Evans and Thomas Lee. Quite how Rooth found the time for all of the work he undertook in addition to his carrying concern is a mystery, especially as the terms of his engagement stated he *"shall devote the whole of his time to the Concerns of the Company"*.

In September 1802, a General Meeting resolved to ask Mr. Fletcher of Clifton, presumably Matthew Fletcher of the coal-owning family in the Irwell valley, to advise on the Tunnel. 3,475 yd were still to cut and 1,000 yd of that which had been cut was incomplete, so very limited

Figure 11 - Brun Clough shaft with an associated reservoir used to supply a Water Engine that operated to haul men and spoil up the shaft.

progress had been made since the floods. They also asked Rooth to provide an estimate of the likely cost of working both ways from Redbrook in addition to at both ends.

Nothing had been reported in the Minutes following John Rooth's examination of the levels in 1801, and in November 1802 the Committee resolved that *"Mr David Whitehead shall be immediately employed to examine the Levels at each end of the Tunnel to ascertain whether they are or are not exactly of one and the same Level and whether the Line of the Tunnel is carrying on in the proper direction."* Nothing was ever minuted about Whitehead's findings either, but a letter written by John Rooth to Robert Firth in 1817 when Rooth was retiring from the company's service, gives details.[5]

Professor R B Schofield has previously published accounts of the supposed surveying errors in Standedge Tunnel, which, with the benefit of access to the Tunnel, appear to be inaccurate and reference has been made to the original document.[6] The actual situation, according to Rooth's letter, was that the eastern end of the summit pound at Marsden and the whole of the completed work on the Tunnel at that end had been constructed two feet above the desired level. Correcting this by cutting the pound and tunnel downwards resulted in the whole of the

---

[5]   *Letter from John Rooth to Robert Firth 26 June 1817, West Yorkshire Archive Service, Huddersfield.*

[6]   *In "Benjamin Outram" (Ch. 6.) and "Huddersfield – a Most Handsome Town" (E A Hilary Haigh, Ed), (Ch. 15), Professor R B Schofield published an account of the supposed surveying errors in Standedge Tunnel. A trip through the Tunnel, which was not possible at the time of his account, suggests that his version of those errors does not fit with the situation on the ground - for example at the western (Diggle) end, which he states was cut too high and had to be lowered, the Tunnel roof is actually quite low and much is in rock, rather than being arched. In addition, the errors that he lists at Marsden, in particular the case of the Marsden end sloping down 3 ft to the workface, would have made it impossible for the work to continue there due to flooding. Reference has been made to the original account and it would appear that whoever originally researched the matter has transposed "East" and "West" where directions are specified, but not "Marsden" and "Diggle", where geographical names are used, resulting in a confusion of the errors at both ends.*

completed arching of the Tunnel at that end, probably around 500 yd, having to be rebuilt. At the western, or Diggle end, the Tunnel had been cut 3 ft below the proper level, necessitating some filling up of the unnecessary cutting, which explains why the headroom there today is tight as Rooth would not want to cut back the Tunnel roof more than he could avoid. No mention was made of the situation at Redbrook. Possibly the most surprising thing about Rooth's letter is to whom it was written. Robert Firth was a member of the Committee from 1798 to 1828, attending a total of 134 meetings in that time. The letter was written by Rooth on his retirement as Agent to the Canal Company in 1817, apparently at Firth's request, to give a full account of what had been done under his management from the year 1800 and the implication is that much of this detail may have remained unknown to the Committee up to that point, although Firth probably knew that something had been amiss for him to ask for an account.

The Proprietors did in fact receive a report from Matthew Fletcher, who provided the General Assembly of November 1802 with his opinion that to work both ways from Redbrook would save two years in completing the Tunnel. The distance involved was

Figure 12 - Robert Firth's memorial stone in the grounds of the Society of Friends Meeting House, Paddock, Huddersfield.

1178 yd. Outram had costed this at £5,000, but Fletcher advised they should allow £8000, clearly being well aware of the tendency for tunnelling costs to escalate. This was approved and in December 1802, the Committee considered that they had a suitable contractor for the task in Jonathan Woodhouse of Ashby-de-la-Zouch, though they decided to refer the matter to a General Meeting in the February. This is a long Minute and there is more than a hint of desperation in their willingness to let the steam engine and all machinery become Woodhouse's property at the end of the contract and in addition to allow him the use of the buildings and land rent-free with bonuses being paid for successful completion - the penalties for failure were to be significantly less than the bonuses. They also stated their intention to continue the eastern end by direct labour. Unfortunately, at the General Meeting, which was very well-attended at the Committee's request, Woodhouse withdrew his offer and asked to be allowed to submit an alternative proposal. This was put to the vote and rejected by a heavy majority of 699 to 399 (one share equalled one vote).

This seems to have finally spelt the end of efforts to restart at Redbrook. It appears that those workings were not re-opened until 1808, when on the report to the Annual Meeting is a footnote: *"N.B. Jul 6th the water in Redbrook Pit was tapped, and on the 16th the old works were examined"* (next section deleted and amended in manuscript) *"when the levels were found to agree but the line differs."* It appears to have taken ten days at the driest time of year to drain the workings and it is quite possible that these had then not been worked since 1797.

At a meeting in March 1805, the Committee approved of John Rooth's supervision of the Tunnel works. From this point on, although the Tunnel was still several years from completion, references to the works seem to disappear from the Minutes. However, progress reports seem to have been given in the papers for the Annual General Meetings, though not all of these survive in the various archives.

It must have been apparent that, even after the second Act of Parliament, there was not going to be sufficient money to complete the Tunnel, as at the Annual Meeting in June 1805, it was resolved to apply for a further Act. A couple of months later, at a further meeting, a figure of £100,000 was specified, nearly twice the original estimate for the Tunnel, which had already been well exceeded. Matters then dragged on, as in January 1806, the Proprietors were still *"re-perusing"* the Bill.

At a Meeting in August 1805, the Proprietors felt the need for another Engineer to inspect the works and it was resolved that *"Mr. Roberts of Dudley"* was to be engaged *"to inspect the state of the works of the canal."* 'Mr. Roberts' may have been Charles Roberts, who was briefly involved with the Manchester, Bolton and Bury Canal, which would fit with the Fletcher connection, but if he ever attended and what he reported is not known.

In the report to the Annual Meeting in June 1806, there were only 331 yd complete at the east end, with a further 1531 yd headed and 452½ yd of *"unbroke ground"*, while at the west end only 510 yd were complete, with 1,535 yd headed and 934½ yd *"unbroke."* At Redbrook, still only 107 yd were complete with a further 50 yd headed, which confirms that all efforts to restart work there had come to nothing. Of the shafts, Brun Clough had recently been completed and an engine house built ready for work. Pule Hoyles (Flint Pit) was still 41 yd short of its final depth.

The third Act of Parliament, passed in March 1806, enabled the Company to raise yet more money to complete the canal by additional calls on the existing shares. Following the approval, a decision was taken in July 1806 to seek a report on the canal by *"one or more engineers."* The two Directors appointed to this task, Thomas Atkinson and Richard Roberts, called

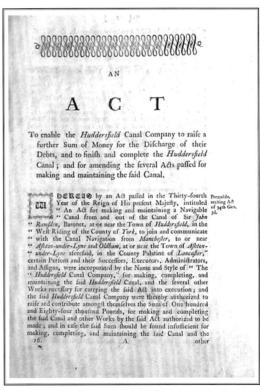

Figure 13 - The first page of the third Act of Parliament for completing the building of the canal.

the next General Meeting on 26th December 1806, at which one of the few references anywhere in the Minutes to the visit of Thomas Telford to the canal was made, when the Committee very politely asked him if he could provide his report in time for the Special General Assembly at the end of January. At that meeting, thanks were given *"to Mr. Walker and Mr. Philips for procuring a report from Mr. Telford,"* so it is most likely Atkinson and Roberts made the first contact by correspondence. 'Walker' is a difficult name, with several among the Directors and Proprietors. 'Philips' may possibly be Samuel Philips, a Merchant of Manchester, but nothing more is known of him. It would be interesting to know how a man like Telford, then probably the best engineer in the country, came to be appointed, as the selection of the best, rather than the cheapest option appears contrary to the Committee's previous practice. It also seems surprising that a very busy man like Telford was prepared to take on the task, as the Company must by that time have developed a poor reputation, judging by their lack of success in attracting contractors.

An abstract of Telford's report, dated January 1807, *"in pursuance of a Resolution made at a Meeting of the Proprietors of the said Canal"* was printed for the Proprietors to consider at their meeting. Telford had looked at the whole canal twice and had every lock filled and emptied. His report starts with the Tunnel and gives a detailed account of each shaft and each length, stating in simple terms *"if you do this and work at this rate, you will complete by this date…"* He gives a final completion date for the whole tunnel of December 1810 and recommends the appointment of a properly qualified supervisor, working under Booth. This report marks a sea change in the building of the canal and must have come as a revelation to the Proprietors and the Committee after the previous years of hopeful forecasts lacking detailed timetables and accurate costings. Although some of the expenditure still to come must have concerned them, they appear to have relied on his plan to complete their canal and on the whole seem to have followed its recommendations. By this time the Proprietors were probably prepared to give their Committee no leeway.

The only other references to Telford in the Minutes are in the April, to the building of what must be Sparth Reservoir, and an agent's house at Woolroad, both of which he had recommended in his report.

It seems doubtful that Telford was appointed to oversee the works and that he ever again visited the canal. None of the three readily available biographies of him so much as mentions the Huddersfield Canal. From this point on, the Committee Minutes, which had already largely avoided the question of progress since 1802, contain no mention of the work to complete the Tunnel and the Locks up from Woolroad to the western end at Diggle. However, the only locally available report to an Annual Meeting from this period, that of 1808, suggests that the Proprietors did receive annual progress reports.[7] That report mentions that at the East end 851 yd were complete with 1,525 headed and only 3½ yd "unbroken". The latter figure explains why they had had to drain the old workings at Redbrook as it would have been impossible to break through until that was done. 1656 yd were finished at the west end, 944 yd headed and 404½ "unbroke." This latter length would produce the Tunnel's famous 'S-bend', when a surveying error resulted in the two lengths of tunnel failing to meet by around 26 ft. The fact that this bend, and thus the meeting of the two lengths, is very close to Redbrook suggests that work never did restart there and that the final length was driven from the West after the eastern end had reached Redbrook. The size of this error makes the comment in the 1808 AGM Report that "the line differs" irrelevant – the error at Redbrook is only a few feet.

On 29th November 1810, disaster struck with the bursting of Black Moss Reservoir with the loss of five lives, according to the Minutes of the 1811 AGM, though other accounts vary. Fortunately for the Tunnel works and the Tunnel End area, the waters of what became known as 'The Black Flood' found their way down the Wessenden Valley. The effect on the Company's finances is not clear, though repairs were not started until 1814 and do not seem to have been completed until 1818.

---

[7] *Report on the Huddersfield Canal Tunnel by John Rooth, to the Company, at their Annual General Meeting, 30th June 1808. John Goodchild Archive.*

Figure 14 - Approaching the 'S-bend' at Redbrook heading towards Diggle. The jack arches pass into natural rock as the Tunnel veers to the left.

Finally, after all these tribulations, at a meeting on 4th April 1811, the Committee asked John Rooth *"to inform the public that the Huddersfield Canal is completely navigable for the conveyance of goods, wares, merchandize and all other materials by advertising the same in the Leeds Intelligencer, the Wakefield and Halifax Journal and in Messrs Wheelers and one of Mr Harrop's Manchester Newspapers."* According to Rooth's letter to Robert Firth, the arching of the Tunnel had been completed in accordance with Telford's estimate and the first boat put through it on 10th December 1810.*(5)*

On 4th April 1811, the official opening was held. It was reported in the Leeds Intelligencer of 8th April, which stated that *"... it was opened on Thursday last, in the presence of a vast concourse of spectators. The Committee, with a number of the Proprietors, entered at the west end a few minutes after ten o'clock in the morning, and made their passage in an hour and forty-four minutes."*

According to Hadfield,[8] the Tunnel had finally cost around £160,000 although in a contemporary handwritten note, a remarkably precise figure of £123,803 9s 2d is given! Even at some £124,000, it is several times the original estimate and it took three times the estimated duration, though this latter figure includes a lengthy period when work was at a standstill.

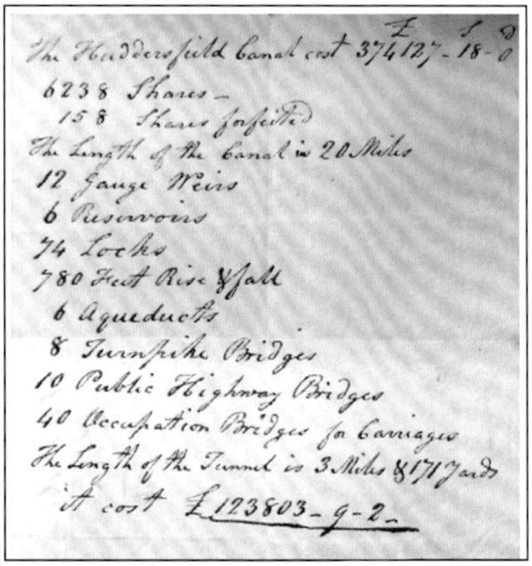

John Goodchild Collection

Figure 15 - A handwritten note summarising the works and costing the Tunnel at exactly £123803 9s 2d!

Soon after the official opening, in May 1811, the Committee directed Rooth to sell off materials left over from the Tunnel works.

In his letter of 1817, Rooth stated that the Tunnel had then been trouble-free, being drained once a year for maintenance, mainly for the clearing of any material fallen from the unlined sections.

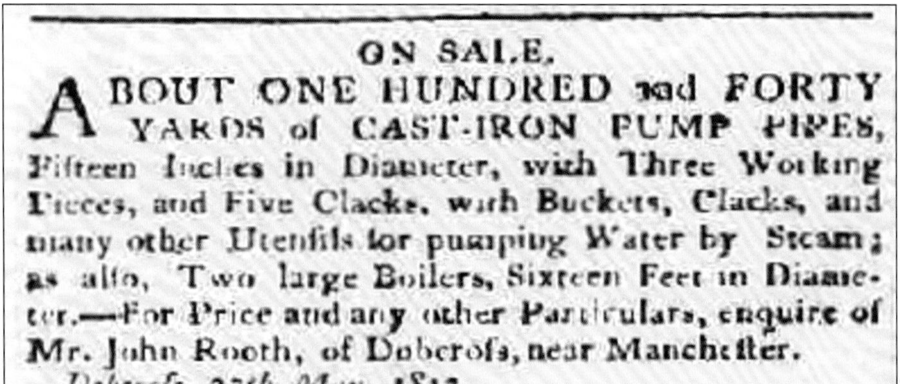

ON SALE.

ABOUT ONE HUNDRED and FORTY YARDS of CAST-IRON PUMP PIPES, Fifteen Inches in Diameter, with Three Working Pieces, and Five Clacks, with Buckets, Clacks, and many other Utenfils for pumping Water by Steam; as alfo, Two large Boilers, Sixteen Feet in Diameter.—For Price and any other Particulars, enquire of Mr. John Rooth, of Dobcrofs, near Manchefter.

Dobcrofs, 27th May, 1812.

Leeds Intelligencer

Figure 16 - Advertisement in Wright's Leeds Intelligencer of May 1812, detailing the sale of materials left over from the Tunnel works.

---

(8) *Hadfield, C. & Biddle, G., (1970) Canals of North West England vol 2 (David & Charles)*

2
The Operation of the Canal Tunnel 1811 - 1843

It was the Company's original intention that boats would pass in the Tunnel and an advertisement for contractors in 1801 included the statement that *"The Tunnel.....is to be made of the clear Width of Nine Feet, except for Two Hundred Yards in Length at the Centre, where it is to be made of the clear Width of Sixteen Feet, to form a Place for Boats to pass each other."*[9] Due to the length quoted, this may well be a reference to Redbrook Wide. Most of the 'Wides' in the Tunnel were probably rebuilt to assist the railway works. One may have been constructed for other reasons; 'Judy', which contains the 'S-bend', created by a surveying error, was probably made to allow boats sufficient room to navigate the bend, though it may have been extended at a later date. How the idea of passing boats could have been operated

Figure 17 - 'White Horse Wide' in Standedge Tunnel looking west. The stone arching suggests that both it and Brun Clough Wide date at least from the early railway works.

[9]   *The Leeds Intelligencer - 09/02/1801 Printed by Thomas Wright*

in an age when there was no means of ready communication between the ends of the Tunnel is hard to imagine and the Committee clearly had second thoughts about it at an early date.

For some reason, with the Tunnel still many years from completion, in December 1804, the Committee decided to look at a number of other tunnels to see how long it took to pass boats through them. By March 1805, the sub-committee were of the opinion that a towpath would be desirable and it was decided to recommend this to the Proprietors at their next General Meeting. In June, the General Assembly asked for further information to be provided at their next meeting in August. This idea of a towpath would, of course, have necessitated enlarging everything so far completed, including taking down all of the arched sections of the Tunnel and rebuilding them. The adjourned General Assembly, to be held in the August, was advertised in the usual newspapers, with the subject of the towpath as its main business. It can only be assumed that the additional information provided had included an estimate of the cost or the time necessary, or perhaps both, as it was *"Resolved by a great majority that a Towing Path shall not be made through the Standedge Tunnel on this Canal."*

Unfortunately, the Canal Company Minutes do not specify what arrangement was adopted at the opening of the Tunnel, but there is no evidence that passing of boats in the Tunnel was attempted. Instead, they appear to have appointed John Bourne, who had been a miner on the Tunnel works at Redbrook as Tunnel Superintendent. There was certainly a separate toll for passing the Tunnel as the Minutes record on 27th September 1811: *"And for each and every Boat which shall be navigated or pass through or along the said Tunnel on the Summit level of the said Canal (except Boats carrying Lime or Limestone) the sum of one shilling and sixpence."* Bourne was responsible for the collection of this sum and controlling boats entering the Tunnel.

John Bourne's son, Thomas, was only 12 years old when *he* became the Tunnel's first traffic regulator. The work involved travelling over the Standedge moors four times a day, seven days a week, and he would hold the post for just eight days short of 37 years, becoming known as 'The Standedge Admiral'. In a letter written after his retirement, Thomas said: *"The first Boat Came through the Canell Came on Tuesday Morning March 26, 1811, And I Travled 37 yrs. Withen 8 dayes, Backwards and Forwards 4 Times a Day Sundays an All unless the Canall Was Stopt and Carid Many Thousands of Money over and Never Was a Penny Short Nor Longer in my hands than is help."* It would appear from this that Bourne collected the Tunnel tolls and counted the boats in and out at each end. There were certainly by-laws of 1812, which enacted that boats should enter at Diggle between 6.00 am and 8.00 am and 5.00 pm and 8.00 pm with entry at Marsden being between 12.00 and 2.00 day and night.[8] How Thomas Bourne managed to do his job in what seems to have been a 24-hour operation is difficult to imagine.

Entry seems to have been controlled initially by means of a 'stopgate' which is mentioned in the following Minute of July 1815, which also seems to have changed the timings: *"Resolved that from and after the first day of August next the Boats navigating the Huddersfield Canal shall enter the west end of the Tunnel at two and ten o'Clock in the morning and at six o'Clock in the evening, and at the east end of the Tunnel at six o'Clock in the morning and at two and ten o'Clock in the evening, to be allowed one quarter of an hour after each stated time for entering the Tunnel before the stopgate is shut and locked and three hours and a half to pass through the Tunnel so as to be clear of the Boats that are ready to enter the other way, and that Vessels not passing the Tunnel within the time above limited be subjected to the same penalties as heretofore."* One stopgate may possibly be that which was formerly sited beneath the footbridge at Tunnel End, where traces of the recess, quoins and 'A' frame may still be seen. Any stopgate at Diggle will have been removed by later alterations, but it would most likely have been close to the Tunnel. At a later date, the stopgates were replaced by winding a chain across the Tunnel mouth, the windlasses at each end still being visible until fairly recent times. A roller still remains at Diggle, over which the chain used to run. *(Figures overleaf)*

Figue 18 - Possible location of the stopgate at Marsden showing the remains of an early design 'A' frame and gate recess (overgrown with ferns).

Figue 19 - A view of the Marsden Portal taken in 1935 showing the chain and windlass. The boat moored in the Tunnel is the inspection craft 'Marsden', formerly Abram Hinchcliffe's 'Gleaner'.

Another activity which may have been envisaged in the Tunnel, particularly that at Redbrook, was the raising of lime up the shafts to improve the moors for agriculture. A Minute of September 1811 on toll charges including the phrase *"conveyed through the Tunnel or discharged therein."* Needless to say, this proposal does not seem to have progressed further.

In 1811, John Rooth passed control of his carrying company to Edmund Buckley, a Saddleworth man who had been his agent in Manchester. With Rooth's involvement in the work on the canal, this may have been a recognition that Buckley had actually been running the company. The Rooths kept a substantial financial stake in the firm, but Buckley would go on to develop the company into a major carrier, by 1817 offering carriage to *"London, Manchester, Liverpool and Bristol"* among other places.[10] Two other firms were also offering a service as in the Canal Company Minutes of August 1812, it was *"Resolved that Messrs Marsden & Welsh the Carriers on this Canal shall have credit for the dues payable to this Company for three months ending the 30th September, the 31st December, the 31st March and the 30th June in every year, the first payment to be due on the 30th September next."* 'Welsh' was Widow Welsh & Sons; Anthony Welsh had been a carrier by road across the North of England until his death in 1810 and his wife and sons had carried on the business. J & L Marsden's origins are uncertain, but this seems to have been their first venture into canal carrying. The three firms would be the mainstays of the flyboat trade, which carried high value goods on a timetabled service, into the 1820s.

The Committee were keen to improve the operation of the Tunnel and as early as 26th June 1816 they minuted *"Resolved that Mr John Rooth be and he is hereby directed to make enquiry as to the expediency of building a Steam Boat to take the other Boats navigating the Huddersfield Canal through Standedge Tunnel..."* and on 24th June 1817 *"A Subscription having been entered into for the purpose of erecting and maintaining a Boat and Steam Engine for navigating*

---

[10]   Baines, Edward (1817). *Directory General & Commercial of the Town and Borough of Leeds.*

Boats through the Tunnel on the summit level of the Huddersfield Canal (instead of what is now called legging).... " It was proposed that there would be a charge not exceeding three shillings for the service.

However, things did not progress rapidly. In December 1817 the Committee received the *"Report of the Committee for conducting the proposed erection of a Steam Engine and Boat for hauling Boats through Standedge Tunnel."* Three of their number had *"entered the Tunnel at the east and in a Boat attached to the Smithy Boat with three Carriers Boats astern, the Smith's Boat Fire being continually blown with the Smith's Bellows and the fire supplyed with best Coal and the three Boats astern having fires in their cabins."* They had apparently passed through twice in the morning and tried again in the afternoon, their conclusion being that they *"were a good deal incommoded by the smoke of the Smiths Boat but not so much as to endanger any person's life,"* which gives a good idea of the attitude to Health and Safety at that time. They went on to say *"Was Pulehoyles, Redbrook and Brunclough Pits uncovered we conceive that no great inconvenience would arise from the smoke of a small Steam Engine to haul Boats through this Tunnel."* This suggests that, in addition to several shafts being filled-in, at least some of the others had been capped over when the Tunnel was completed.

Again, it would appear that little or nothing came of this experiment, as in November 1821 a Mr John Radley of Oldham *"... laid before them his Plans for propelling Boats through the summit Tunnel of the Canal,"* and then in June 1822 they minuted *"The Committee having agreed to allow Mr Wharton Engineer of the Manchester and Salford Waterworks Company the sum of Fifty pounds towards trying an experiment with a Steam Boat through the summit Tunnel of this Canal..........Resolved that no further sum be allowed to him on that account,"* from which it appears not to have been a success.
They further *"Resolved that the Steam Boat upon Mr Raistricks Chain principle be tried by him through the Summit Tunnel at an expence not exceeding Twenty pounds in addition to that already incurred."* Raistrick was presumably John Raistrick who was their Engineer for many years.

He appears to have persevered for some time as in February 1823:
"Mr Raistrick upon being allowed to navigate the Tunnel and summit Level of the Canal with a Steam Boat free from dues for ten years having offered to put one on for the purpose of haling Boats through the Tunnel upon a better principle than they are now taken and at an expence not exceeding three shillings per Boat. Resolved that the offer be accepted and that Mr Raistrick do immediately proceed to carry the same into effect." This offer was presumably pursued, and in December 1824 the regulations to be adopted *"in regard to Vessels passing through the Tunnel by means of the Steam Vessel"* were left to three Directors to arrange. The Minutes are silent on the outcome, but as Thomas Bourne seems to have continued to cross the moors until around 1848, the venture can not have been a long-term success. A number of Minutes of 1826/7 note the removal of Tunnel dues on various cargoes, which must cast further doubt on whether a towage service was then being provided.

One Minute that can not be ignored is from February 1824, when the Committee *"Resolved That it is the opinion of this Committee that the earnings of the Canal for this year appearing fully to warrant a Dividend of One pound per share it be recommended to the next General Meeting........"* - finally, over thirty years after the Proprietors put down their initial deposits, any that still held their shares were going to see a small return on their investment. The situation was so momentous that in June 1824, the Committee became almost triumphal and it was *"Resolved that an obelisk be erected at the place where the Turnpike Road on Standedge crosses the line of the Tunnel on the summit level of the Canal with a suitable inscription thereon, the expence thereof not to exceed twenty pounds....."* Again, we do not know if this was ever carried out, but it was still a live issue in the November when a design was produced and approved and Raistrick was to get it erected *"so as the Expence do not exceed Fifty Pounds."* The turnpike road referred to would have been the third to be constructed, on the line of the present A62, which would have placed the obelisk at the western end of the cutting, overlooking Brun Clough Reservoir. No trace remains today, were it ever erected, but the road has been widened considerably over the years and the obelisk may have been demolished.

The increased profitability of the canal is reflected in a slow growth in the number of carriers. The short-lived Huddersfield Shipping Company started to operate a flyboat service from Engine Bridge in Huddersfield around 1825, but they were gone by 1829, probably due to having over-reached themselves. They were replaced at Engine Bridge by John Kenworthy & Co, a Manchester-based company, but offering services as far afield as London.

Another idea for improvement appears in a Minute of February 1829: *"Resolved that Mr Raistrick see the Carriers upon this Canal and informs them the Committee will entertain any suggestions that they may have to offer respecting conveying the haling Horses through the Tunnel in a Boat."* Again, nothing more is mentioned.

In May 1833, the Tunnel toll was taken off for all vessels navigating the whole length of the line.

A further indication that all attempts to provide a steam tug had failed comes in April 1834, when it is *"Resolved that Mr Raistrick be authorized to call the sub Committee at Huddersfield to consider of the propriety of offering a premium or premiums, not more than One hundred Guineas for an effectual way of haling Boats through the Tunnel,"* and in November 1834: *"Mr Kenworthy* (probably the Director of this name rather than the Carrier) *having recommended that it be tried whether some facility may not be given in passing Boats through the Tunnel by admitting the Water into one end of the Tunnel at the time of the Boats passing through the same so as to occasion a current which will be serviceable to the navigating of the Boats...."* In May 1835 they sent Raistrick to the Trent and Mersey Canal to examine *".....the mode now adopted for.....passing Boats through the Harecastle Tunnel and that he do consider how far any improvements he may observe may be adopted on this Canal."* Again little seems to have happened as a result of his visit.

It would be June 1838 before the Committee recommended another dividend, this time of two pounds per share, but from this point on, dividends became regular. Indeed, in 1840 they began to pay them half-yearly and by June of 1841 the Minutes are sufficiently bullish as to refer to *"the usual half-yearly dividend"*! Sadly, by 1843, the tide had turned and no dividend was paid. The Minutes of the Huddersfield Canal Company come to an end in October 1843 on something of a cliffhanger with the Committee apparently on the verge of concluding an Agreement with the Manchester and Leeds Railway.

The Manchester and Leeds Railway had opened its line through the Calder Valley in 1841, avoiding Huddersfield, but the effect on the profits of the Huddersfield Canal Company was soon felt. Traffic on the canal had peaked in the late 1830s, and by 1840 no less than seven firms were competing for the valuable flyboat trade, all of them operating daily, and many with connections as far afield as London.[11] These included major national carriers such as Pickfords, Carver & Co (sometimes listed as Carver, Driver & Co) and John Kenworthy & Co More regional were Barnby, Faulkner & Co, Buckley, Kershaw & Co (descended from John Rooth's original business), Thompson, McKay & Co and T & W Marsden (the business now being run by the sons of the founders), though some of these offered carriage to London.

This was the trade which had enabled the Company to at last pay dividends to its long-suffering shareholders, but it was this high-value traffic on which the new railway had an immediate effect. Many of the carrying firms, realising that the most profitable traffic would leave the canals for the faster railways, rushed to involve themselves in railway business, with the railway companies often demanding that they give up their canal activities in exchange for allowing them to trade.

━●━

---

[11]   *Pigot & Co, (1841). Royal National and Commercial Directory and Topography of the Counties of York, Leicester & Rutland, Lincoln, Northampton and Nottingham.*

3
The First Railway Tunnel
The Nicholson Tunnel 1843 - 1865

The Huddersfield Canal Company had very quickly entered into negotiations with the Manchester and Leeds Railway, which had surveyed a branch from its line through the Calder Valley into Huddersfield in 1843 and announced its intention to seek an Act of Parliament. The branch would have terminated somewhere in the Turnbridge/Aspley area at the bottom of town. The merchants and industrialists of Huddersfield, some of them the same people who served on the Committee of the Canal Company, were not happy with this proposal, which they saw as sidelining Huddersfield, because its low level would have prevented the future development of a through line towards Manchester. The Manchester and Leeds Company responded with some unwise statements about the value of Huddersfield as a destination, which helped to stir up opposition to their proposal. Public Meetings were called and it was decided to form a separate railway company, the Huddersfield and Manchester Railway and Canal Company. The new company would take over the Huddersfield Canal Company and an attractive deal was offered to its shareholders, either in the form of railway shares or cash.

The new company planned a through line with a tunnel adjacent to the Canal Tunnel and would benefit from that in the building of its own tunnel. An announcement appeared in the Leeds Intelligencer in April 1844, advertising 20,000 shares of £30 each, for which it would be necessary to deposit £1 10s. on each share.[12] The advertisement named a provisional committee, including a number of people from the Sheffield and Manchester Railway, which was originally expected to be a partner. The Chairman and several committee members were from the Canal Company. In May, the Leeds Times revealed that options on the whole of the shares had been taken in the first week.[13]

---

[12]   *Leeds Intelligencer - 20/04/1844, 27/04/1844, 04/05/1844.*
[13]   *Leeds Times - 04/05/1844.*

By the end of 1844, the necessary documents had been deposited and at the end of April 1845, there was a week of celebration in Huddersfield. On Saturday 25th, news reached the town that the Act had passed its Committee stage. The church bells were rung and a band toured the town.[14] The Act was finally approved by Parliament in July and the ceremony of cutting the first sod of the railway took place near Deighton on 10th October 1845.[15]

Work on the first Standedge railway tunnel started under the overall control of Alfred S Jee, the engineer for the Huddersfield and Manchester Company. The contractor, Thomas Nicholson, had come straight from the building of the first Woodhead Tunnel on the Sheffield and Manchester Railway and the first Standedge railway tunnel is often referred to as the Nicholson Tunnel. It was always intended that a second tunnel would one day be built, indeed there was provision in the Act both for the Company to build one, and for the Board of Trade to

Figure 20 - The Crest of the Huddersfield & Manchester Railway & Canal Company adorning the King's Head public house at Huddersfield Railway Station.

---

[14] *Bradford Observer - 01/05/1845*

[15] *Leeds Intelligencer - 18/10/1845*

require one to be built if it felt necessary. Unlike at Woodhead, where the second tunnel was built once the first had been completed, it would be some years before the second tunnel was built, but the entrance and first few yards at each end of the second tunnel were built at this time.

Nicholson used five of the shafts which had been used in building the Canal Tunnel, but first enlarged these, starting in October 1845. In October 1846 the death of a miner engaged in this work was reported, killed by a stone falling from a bucket as it was being raised.[16] In addition to the shafts, a number of adits were constructed from the Canal Tunnel and, according to a contemporary account, the tunnel was built working from 18 faces, suggesting 8 adits and the two ends.[17] Work on the tunnel proper started in November 1846.

Figure 21 - Unimproved adit No. 26 connecting the Canal Tunnel to Nicholson's railway tunnel; note the minor adit bottom left which connects through to the second, Nelson railway tunnel.

---

[16]   *Leeds Mercury - 03/10/1846*
[17]   *Leeds Intelligencer - 21/07/1849*

At first the work must have proceeded using the same methods as in the Canal Tunnel, by hand drilling and the use of black powder, but it was reported in several newspapers in March 1847 that experiments had been carried out with the newly-invented gun cotton, which was found to be roughly four times as powerful as gunpowder.[18] This must have been one of the first projects where this new technology was tried, as there were many observers of the tests, and a dinner was held for them at the New Inn in Marsden that evening.

Figure 22 - New Inn at Marsden still stands, albeit extended somewhat.

It was around this time that agreement was reached to merge the company with the London and North Western Railway (LNWR), and an Act of Parliament was passed in July 1847.[19] Despite this, the Huddersfield company seems to have remained administratively separate until the whole line was completed, and for some time thereafter seems to have formed a separate division within the larger

---

[18] *Leeds Mercury, Manchester Courier - 20/03/1847*
[19] *Leeds Intelligencer - 19/06/1847*

company, as did some other constituents. A report to the Annual General Meeting in August 1847 stated that it was hoped to complete the whole line by May 1849.[20]

Nicholson's working practices apparently left something to be desired. An extract from the Minutes of the Company dated 1st March 1848 report an inspection of the Canal Tunnel, and reveal that he had previously been given notice to improve several areas.[21] Despite this a number of the headings and sections of the Canal Tunnel remained insecure and large quantities of spoil were being allowed to fall into the canal, which had already had to be cleaned out several times. It was resolved that Nicholson should make further improvements. Around the same time there were a number of cases in the local Magistrates Court against Nicholson for reducing his workers' wages without notice and allegedly making illegal deductions from their pay.[22]

Under changes made to the Tunnel Regulations in March 1848, after the Canal Company had become part of the Huddersfield and Manchester Railway and Canal Company, Agents at each end of the Tunnel gave a certificate to the *"last boat at each turn entering the tunnel, also a red signal lamp, and the practice of sending a man through with the boats to be discontinued."* Judging by the date, this would appear to coincide with the end of Thomas Bourne's journeys over Standedge and it speaks of a man accompanying the boats rather than walking over the hill, though it would presumably still have been necessary for the boat horses to be taken over. The purpose of the red signal lamp is unclear, although at this date the first railway tunnel was under construction, so it may have served as an indication to those operating the boats removing spoil from the tunnel that the last boat had passed and they could freely move their boats until the traffic was due to pass in the opposite direction.[21]

---

[20]   *Leeds Intelligencer - 28/08/1847*

[21]   *Public Record Office - RAIL 308/7*

[22]   *Leeds Times - 15/01/1848, 12 /02/1848*

An illustration of the progress in the planning of civil engineering works, and the extent to which the use of the Canal Tunnel had assisted in the construction, is that the first trial train through the tunnel was run in June 1849, followed by the official opening ceremony on the 13th July 1849 and the start of public traffic on 1st August.[23]

A number of minor place names disappeared during the various tunnel works, including the hamlet of Waterside, now only commemorated by one of the former bridge-sites on the top pound. This seems to have vanished around the time of the first railway tunnel as it appears on a hand-drawn map of 1801 and people were apparently still living there on the 1841 Census, including some boatmen. By the 1851 Census, there does not appear to be any mention of it and the first Ordnance Survey® (OS), published in 1854, but surveyed 1848-50, does not mark it, though both of the bridges on the top pound of the canal, today marked by narrows, remain. The disappearance of the hamlet suggests that much material was taken directly from the tunnel and either tipped between canal and river on what became the Tunnel End Sidings area or between canal and railway. The name "Waterside" appears to transfer to the area alongside Tunnel End reservoir.

RAILWAY PLANT, MATERIALS, &c.,

Used in the Construction and Completion of Standedge Tunnel, in Marsden, and the adjoining railway works, amongst which may be enumerated five 25-horse power high-pressure STEAM ENGINES. (These Engines have all wrought-iron Axles, and are capable of being made from 15 to 20 horses' power more, with an extra Cylinder. No. 1 Engine has a 30-horse power; Nos. 2, 3, 4, and 5, have two Boilers each, 24 feet long; 6 feet diameter, and circular ends, all in excellent working condition, and nearly new.) Also one 12-horse power high-pressure Steam Engine, which has a capital Mortar Mill, double Rollers, revolving Iron Pans, and Saw Mill attached; nearly 400 tons of light and strong temporary Rails, Chairs, well-built and powerful Locomotive Goods Engine, Tender, &c., &c., which has had but little wear; excellent three-inch capstan Ropes, 200 yards flat Ropes; large quantity of Scrap Iron, of excellent quality; 19 Canal Boats; a large quantity of Memel, Oak, and Elm Timber; Scantlings, Planks, Prop Wood, Sleepers, Laggins, broken-up Timber; Oak, Larch, and other Timber, in the round; Balks, a great number of Centres, of different spans, for Arches, Tunnels, and Culverts; five sets of capital Head Gears; capital Weighing Machine, to weigh nine tons, by Firm Grates, 12 Smiths' Anvils, several hundred Waggons and Lurries, 30 Turn-Tables, Pile Engine, double speed and single purchase Crabs, cast-iron Pumps, five Capstans, of the best make and quality; folding Doors, pair of large Pulley Wheels, with about 500 yards of half-inch Chain; Cranes, a great number of Striking Hammers, Quarry and Mining Picks, Buckling, Crab, and other Chains, Pulleys, Vices, Tongs; 700 Drills, of the best Iron, and steeled with the best steel; Mattocks, Anvils, Smiths' Bellows, both flat and cylindrical; Scales, Oil Cistern and Pump, a new six-inch Waggon, Spring Cart, two strong Carts, excellent Whitechapel, Gig, Harness, Bay Mare, Cart Harness, patent Chaff Engines, and a great variety of valuable effects.

Detailed particulars are being prepared in Catalogues, which may be obtained, five days prior to the sale, at the Offices of the Auctioneer, 68, Cross Street, King Street, in Manchester. Catalogues will also be forwarded to gentlemen at a distance, upon receipt of six Postage Stamps.

P.S. The principal Plant is within five minutes' walk of the Marsden Station, and also adjoins the Canal and Turnpike Road, which will render the goods easy of transit.

ORDER OF SALE, VIZ:—

FIRST DAY.—Part Timber, Sleepers, Waggons, part of Smiths' Shops, Wrought and Cast Metal, five Canal Boats, &c.

SECOND DAY.—Part Timber, part of Smiths' Shops, Crabs, Chains, Wrought and Cast Metal, Bay Mare, Whitechapel, Gig, Waggon, Carts, Harness, Chaff Engines, &c.

THIRD DAY.—Part of Timber, Stores, Tools, Turn-Tables, heavy Implements, Weighing Machine, Waggons, Rails, Crabs, &c.

FOURTH DAY.—This day's sale will commence at Wool road, about ten minutes' walk from the Saddleworth Station; consequently, parties coming by rail must alight at this station. The order of selling will be 14 Canal Boats; five 25-horse power Steam Engines; one ditto 12-horse ditto, with Mortar Mill; Engine Houses, Sheds, Buildings, Capstans, Guide Rods, Ropes, &c.

FIFTH DAY.—Remainder of the Timber, Wrought Iron, Scrap Iron, Bars, Tools, Stores, and miscellaneous effects.

The morning trains leave Manchester at 8 45 and 10 30 a.m., and Leeds at 9 30 and 10 45 a.m. This sale will commence each morning at a few minutes after eleven o'clock, to give time for the arrival of the trains from Manchester, Leeds, Birmingham, Sheffield, Huddersfield, Bolton, &c., which stop at Marsden Station.

Huddersfield Chronicle

Figure 23 - The Chronicle's detailed advertisement for the sale of plant and equipment.

[23] Leeds Intelligencer - 23/06/1849, 14/07/1849, Bradford Observer - 26/07/1849

A series of sales of the plant and equipment no longer required were held at Tunnel End and at Woolroad over five working days between Wednesday 24th April and Monday 29th April 1850. The advertisement included two lots of boats: 5 boats to be sold at Marsden and 14 boats to be sold at Woolroad.[24] A final sale took place in February 1852 at which a further three narrow boats were sold.[25] Thomas Nicholson purchased a number of quarries in Marsden and Linthwaite and some of the boats that had been used, and went into the business of selling stone, although he was still referred to as a Railway Contractor.[26] He seems to have rented the boatyard at Woolroad from the LNWR and appears in some directories as a boat builder.[27] There are records in the archives of negotiations for a wharf near Tunnel End, intended to be adjacent to where a lane then crossed the canal at the narrows which still remain close to the railway bridge, though ultimately nothing seems to have come of these.[28] One of Nicholson's boats was responsible for closing the Canal Tunnel in April 1855, when its load shifted and it sank, leaving the leggers standing in the water for over 3 hours.[29] It is interesting to note that the report states that 1½ miles of the Tunnel had to be drained to recover the boat, which confirms that stop planks could be inserted in several places – some of these sites can probably still be identified at the present day by rings in the tunnel roof. (According to George Holroyd, once Ganger for the London Midland Scottish who Geoff Brown interviewed, there were three such places.)

Nicholson appears in the surviving Minutes of the LNWR committee responsible for the canal on several occasions through 1856 and into 1857, usually complaining about toll rates, but in November 1857, the

---

[24] *Huddersfield Chronicle - 20/04/1850*

[25] *Huddersfield Chronicle - 31/01/1852*

[26] *Various references, eg. Huddersfield Chronicle - 07/01/1854, 05/08/1854 and 13/01/1855*

[27] *Slater's Commercial Directory of Durham, Northumberland & Yorkshire, (1855)*

[28] *Correspondence between Carter (Canal Manager), Brook (Director) and Nicholson. (1850) - Geoff Brown obtained a copy from the Boat Museum, Ellesmere Port; presumably now in the Waterways Archives.*

[29] *Huddersfield Chronicle - 28/04/1855*

Huddersfield Chronicle advertised a sale of his assets.[30][31] His quarry business appears to have become bankrupt and he returned to railway contracting. He died in 1861 at the age of 70, being run down by a contractor's engine while inspecting a railway viaduct at Ingleton.[32]

The Act for the railway tunnel had made provision for the use of an electric telegraph to regulate traffic, but it also seems to have been the practice that a pilot engine was used, being attached to a train entering the tunnel, the normal rule being that no train could enter without the pilot engine. However, *(see below)* providing the pilot engine was present at that end, more than one train could be admitted in the one direction, a message being sent by the telegraph to inform the signalman at the other end what train or trains had been despatched.

A report by Jee, dated 13th May 1850, and addressed to *"the Directors of the Huddersfield and Manchester Railway Company"* found a number of areas in the railway tunnel which he considered to be unsafe. [33] That this was the case is confirmed by a report in the Huddersfield Chronicle in May 1851 that the pilot engine had been damaged by striking a fallen rock.

The pilot engine was apparently kept in the short length of the second tunnel when not required. The LNWR seem to have taken the view that it would be a waste of money to provide one of their better engines for the purpose, but by 1852 it was developing something of a reputation. In November, the Huddersfield Chronicle reported on *"The Standedge Tunnel Pilot Engine and its Infirmities"* concluding *"This poor and aged machine....is in a sad way. It is monstrous that a wealthy body, like the London and North Western Railway Company, should allow a machine, which is inflicted with all the ills that engines are heir to,*

[30] LNWR Minutes (1855-68). Copy held by Huddersfield Canal Society; original by Waterways Archives, Leeds.

[31] Huddersfield Chronicle - 21/11/1857

[32] Obituary in Huddersfield Chronicle - 18/05/1861

[33] Geoff Brown's papers. Copy originally obtained from the British Transport Commission Archives.

to be applied to its present service. The thing is unsound and should, at its advanced age, be allowed to retire from active life, and give place to a better and safer guide. "[34] It is interesting to speculate what locomotive of *"advanced age"* had been provided as this date is only just over 20 years from the Rainhill Trials and the building of Stephenson's 'Rocket', the ancestor of the LNWR's locomotive fleet.

There were also problems with the Canal Tunnel. In an extract from the Minutes of the North Eastern Sub-Committee, of the North Eastern Division, held 4th February 1856, Mr Carter (presumably Robert S Carter, the Company's Canal Manager) reported that *"the Standedge Canal Tunnel is receiving much damage from the rock and shale falling, which he conceives is owing to the working of the Railway traffic in the adjoining Tunnel."* It was ordered *"That Mr Carter consult with Mr Woodhouse and report further to the Committee."*[31] The LNWR must have called in J E Errington *(1806-1862),* an eminent railway engineer, and a copy of a letter from him dated 12th November 1856 states that the Canal Tunnel was *"... never of sufficient strength, ..."* but that it had been badly-affected by the construction of the railway tunnel. He detailed a number of areas in the tunnel which he considered to be in danger of imminent collapse.[33] Several newspapers subsequently carried a notice of the closure of the Canal Tunnel for repairs.[35]

Sadly, the closure put another 'nail in the coffin' of the canal's trade. Most of the flyboat carriers listed earlier at the canal's peak in the 1840s had already gone by 1850, but since 1855, the Aire and Calder Navigation Company (ACN) had been trying to get a carrying trade to Manchester re-established by way of the canal, using the Huddersfield warehouse and possibly other assets of Pickfords' local flyboat operation. The latter seems to have lasted on the Huddersfield Canal until around that date, being listed in a Directory of 1853, unlike the vast bulk of their canal operations, which they rapidly abandoned in

---

[34]   *Huddersfield Chronicle - 06/11/1852*

[35]   *Leeds Intelligencer - 14/02/1857*

their rush to become a railway carrier.[36] They had particular links to the LNWR and it is possible that goods facilities took time to develop on the new line and that their flyboat traffic was thus continued for a period with the agreement of the LNWR. The ACN had also leased a warehouse at Manchester, appointed an agent and bought 14 narrow boats, into which goods would be transhipped at Huddersfield from their wide-beam craft. The closure of the tunnel, which the ACN company suspected was unnecessary and designed by the LNWR to hamper a trade which competed with their railway, resulted in the venture being discontinued in the October.[37]

Into the 1860s there are increasing numbers of reports in the Press of minor accidents in and around the railway tunnel, some of which resulted in damage and injury, and all of which caused delay and inconvenience, and it must have been clear to the LNWR that the second tunnel was now badly-needed.

Figure 24 - Detail of an early view of the Diggle area showing the portal of the Nicholson Tunnel in the distance. Note the abandoned canal basins. Diggle Paper Mill is on the right.

[36]   *Whellan's Manchester & Salford Directory. (1853)*

[37]   *Hadfield, Charles, (1972). "The Canals of Yorkshire and North-east England",
      (David & Charles). Also an advertisement in the Huddersfield Chronicle -
      27/10/1855 (and weekly for some weeks after).*

4
The Second Railway Tunnel
The Nelson Tunnel 1865 - 1890

The building of a second railway tunnel through Standedge was announced in November 1865, as part of the London and North Western Railway (New Lines) Bill.[38] Why a new Act was required is not clear, as provision had been made for the construction of a second tunnel in the original Act and indeed the first few yards at each end had been built. Probably the powers in the Act had lapsed, or the answer may lie in the section of the Bill relating to *"additional capital"*.

Thomas Nelson was the contractor for the second tunnel. A Scot, born c.1807, he had worked his way up from being a mason under George Stephenson to carry out a number of large contracts for the LNWR. The Engineer was Joseph Buck, a career engineer with the railway company. In February 1868 it was announced that Nelson's bid of £121,500 had been accepted and the contract would start *"forthwith"*.[39] Certainly some work was going on by March, when the same paper reported an accident to a man employed by a Mr Wilson, who was described as the Contractor for the new tunnel; the man had been unloading materials at Tunnel End Sidings.[40] By May, a number of buildings were under construction for workshops and accommodation and in July the paper announced the arrival of a steam tug.[41] This had apparently arrived by canal from the Saddleworth direction, but when tried in the tunnel, had trouble generating steam due to the confined space and the men had been forced to leg it through, taking some four hours.[42] It would need to be modified to improve the draughting of the fire, possibly by shortening the funnel.

---

[38]   *Leeds Mercury - 18/11/1865*
[39]   *Huddersfield Examiner - 15/02/1868*
[40]   *Huddersfield Weekly Examiner - 21/03/1868*
[41]   *Huddersfield Examiner - 16/05/1868*
[42]   *Huddersfield Examiner - 04/07/1868*

The new tunnel was situated beyond the first tunnel and it was necessary to construct adits beneath the operational railway in order to move spoil to the Canal Tunnel. The actual method of moving the spoil through these confined spaces is unknown, though when the equipment was sold at the end of the contract, a large number of iron skips were included. Another unknown is when the 'Cathedral' was constructed and why. This is a full-height cross adit, which links the two railway tunnels at the midpoint and it is reinforced with iron ribs. No reference to it has been found in any of the accounts of the building of the tunnels and the only mention of it in Geoff Brown's notes are to the later existence of a platelayers' shelter in the space provided.

It does not align with any adit to the Canal Tunnel and the question must be: 'When and why was it built?' To construct it as part of the second tunnel would disrupt traffic in the first tunnel for no apparent purpose - could it have been built as part of the first tunnel works to provide two potential working faces, in the same way that the two entrances were built at that time?

Safety was still poor by modern standards. In September, a miner was burned after several charges misfired a little to the west of Flint Pit. He was withdrawing them, unwisely using an iron implement, when one of them fired.[43] Oddly, in the light of the experiments with gun cotton in the earlier tunnel, it was said to be gunpowder that was involved. Around the same time, canal traffic was suspended for over nine weeks due to drought, resuming in late September. This was said to be probably the longest such stoppage in the history of the canal.[44]

Meantime, the catalogue of accidents in and around the original tunnel continued, some of which suggest poor operating practices, such as in October 1868, when the pilot engine was damaged by colliding with a goods train which had entered the tunnel as part of a shunting manoeuvre at Diggle.

---

[43]   *Huddersfield Examiner - 19/09/1868*
[44]   *Huddersfield Examiner - 03/10/1868*

Oddly, it appears to have been the practice to uncouple the pilot engine inside the tunnel, presumably because of a lack of space at both ends of the tunnel. This manoeuvre was apparently carried out whilst the train was moving, for it to run out onto the other track, ready to take a train back the other way. The points would then be switched back so that the train which it had been piloting could continue its journey.[45]

In February 1870, when the second tunnel was already under construction, a collision occurred at Marsden due to a telegraph message being misunderstood and the signalman having set the points in anticipation of the pilot engine running out to couple onto a waiting train, instead an express emerged and collided with the other train.

In 1869, two incidents resulted in the closure of the Canal Tunnel. The first was the sinking of a Nelson steam tug, the 'Lively Kitten', when its crew had to be rescued from the water and the boat refloated.[46] This was quickly followed by the sinking of a boat owned by the Manchester, Sheffield and Lincolnshire Railway and leased to a John Higginbottom of Marple who was carrying limestone. The boat was struck by a rock weighing some three tons, dislodged by blasting, close to the Marsden end.[47] Very soon afterwards, a large fall, a mile and a quarter from Diggle, reduced the depth of the water at that point to eighteen inches, stopping all traffic for a day and a half.[48]

A number of similar events continued into 1870, finally resulting in all of Nelson's boats being blockaded in the tunnel in the February by a fall at 'Hell Kettle' near to Marsden, which was shortly followed by a fall towards the Diggle end.[49] Even when not troubled by falling rock, all did not necessarily go well when the boats and the crew of a steamer at the Diggle end had a narrow escape from suffocation from the use of poor quality coke.[50] At the same time, it was reported

---

[45]   *Huddersfield Examiner - 24/10/1868*

[46]   *Huddersfield Weekly Examiner - 23/10/1869*

[47]   *Huddersfield Weekly Examiner - 06/11/1869*

[48]   *Huddersfield Examiner - 18/12/1869*

[49]   *Huddersfield Weekly Examiner - 19/02/1870*

[50]   *Huddersfield Weekly Examiner - 23/04/1870*

that the 'Wonder', a boat owned by John Brierley of Slaithwaite had become stuck in the Tunnel. This seems to have been due to the boat having spread with age, rather than a problem with the Tunnel, but the boat was capable of returning down the Diggle Locks to the boatyard at Woolroad for repairs. The troubles in the Canal Tunnel culminated in spectacular fashion in the August, when a boatman named Archibald Hoole, employed by Nelson, was killed by the explosion of two cans of blasting powder, each of half a hundredweight. It was thought that he had been tampering with this cargo at the time. Tragically, his body was recovered from the water by his brother, who was also a boatman.[51] This was said to be the first fatal accident on the works.

Throughout the building of the Tunnel, there are reports in the various newspapers of drunkenness and fighting among the navvies, and early in 1870, as the works neared completion, the 'Examiner' reported that there had been several instances of men running up debts and then simply disappearing.[52]

Actual progress on the tunnel works is difficult to judge, as reports in the press are limited to accidents and incidents involving the workforce and there are few reports on the works themselves – probably because long tunnels were by now commonplace. In 4th June 1870, the Huddersfield Chronicle briefly reported that the tunnel was expected to be fully driven in about four months.[53] It further reported that "... not a single person has been killed in the work, ..." a tribute to the progress made in civil engineering. This appears to be a case of speaking too soon, however, as on the 25th of that month, the same paper reported a miner being crushed by a falling rock - he had been taken to the Infirmary with "slight hopes of recovery, ..." and of course there would shortly be the case of Archibald Hoole. In October, it was reported that the Tunnel would be ready for inspection by 1st December.[54]

---

[51]   *Huddersfield Examiner - 27/08/1870*
[52]   *Huddersfield Weekly Examiner - 12/02/1870*
[53]   *Huddersfield Chronicle - 04/06/1870*
[54]   *Huddersfield Weekly Examiner - 29/10/1870*

There appears to have been no great ceremony around the opening of the new tunnel, which was actually inspected on 5th January 1871.(55) The opening simply consisted of a number of platelayers connecting the new tracks at both Marsden and Diggle on the morning of Sunday 12th February, following which the earlier tunnel was closed *"for an indefinite period"* to allow for repairs to be made.(56)

The Contractors had already begun to sell off their equipment in November 1870, with a listing in the 'Examiner' of materials including steam engines, the four steam narrowboats and 24 open boats with 200 iron skips and much more.(57) On 21st January 1871 the Leeds Mercury carried a notice of a final sale by Mr. Thomas Nelson of Contractor's Plant *"used in making the new Standedge Tunnel, now completed"*.

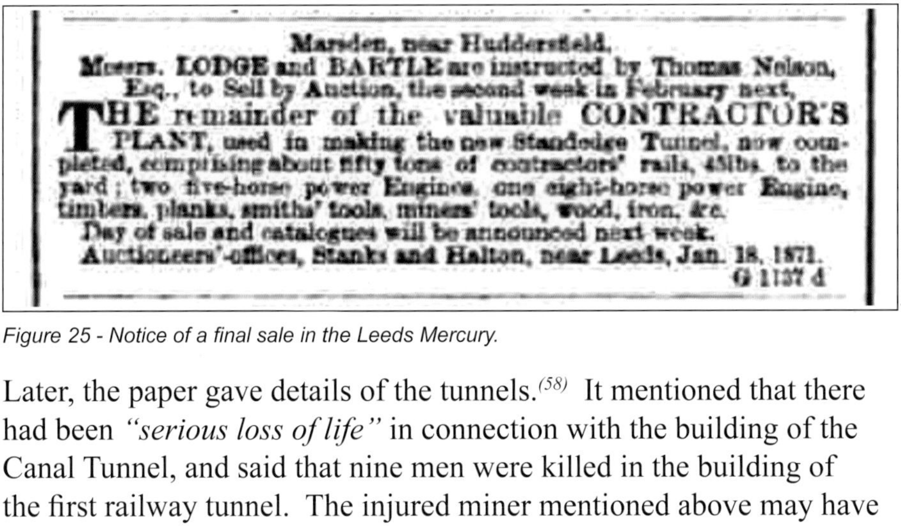
Marsden, near Huddersfield.
Messrs. LODGE and BARTLE are instructed by Thomas Nelson, Esq., to Sell by Auction, the second week in February next,
THE remainder of the valuable CONTRACTOR'S PLANT, used in making the new Standedge Tunnel, now completed, comprising about fifty tons of contractors' rails, 45lbs. to the yard; two five-horse power Engines, one eight-horse power Engine, timbers, planks, smiths' tools, miners' tools, wood, iron, &c.
Day of sale and catalogues will be announced next week.
Auctioneers'-offices, Stanks and Halton, near Leeds, Jan. 18, 1871.
G 1137 d

Leeds Mercury

Figure 25 - Notice of a final sale in the Leeds Mercury.

Later, the paper gave details of the tunnels.(58) It mentioned that there had been *"serious loss of life"* in connection with the building of the Canal Tunnel, and said that nine men were killed in the building of the first railway tunnel. The injured miner mentioned above may have survived, as the account went on to say that only one life had been lost in the course of the new tunnel. Thomas Nelson and Sons had succeeded in completing the work six months before the specified date. For some reason, the new tunnel was quoted as 5,345 yd long - a yard

(55) *Huddersfield Chronicle - 07/01/1871*

(56) *Huddersfield Chronicle - 18/02/1871*

(57) *Huddersfield Weekly Examiner - 05/11/1870*

(58) *Leeds Mercury - 04/03/1871*

less than the earlier railway tunnel, though this does not quite agree with the figure generally quoted. Spoil had been carried away to the Canal Tunnel through 21 adits constructed beneath the first railway tunnel. 25 boats and 4 steam tugs had been used.

Towards the end of March it was reported that the repair work to the first railway tunnel was expected to be complete in three weeks time.[59] Nearly ten tons of soot had been removed. Finally, on the 6th May, it was reported that the tunnels had been worked separately for the first time on the previous Sunday. It was intended that a 'block' system would be used with only one train being allowed in each tunnel at any one time.

With the opening of the tunnel, a relative silence descended, with only an occasional incident reported in the Press. In April 1872 there was a report of an inquest on a legger drowned in the Canal Tunnel, then little until February 1881, when the engine of a Manchester-bound train failed in the tunnel.[60][61] The following year, there is a passing reference in the Leeds Times to the building of the Micklehurst loop line, which was part of a scheme to widen the line between Stalybridge and Huddersfield to four tracks and which would eventually bring about the construction of the third and final railway tunnel.[62]

On a somewhat lighter note, there is a mention of an early pleasure trip through the Canal Tunnel, when *"30 mill owners and Commissioners of the Wessenden Reservoir"* chartered the boat 'John' on the 12th August 1888.[63] Despite torrential rain, an *"excellent lunch"* was served under canvas at Marsden before the trip set off, taking two and a quarter hours for the journey to Diggle, following which many of the party walked back to the New Inn at Marsden for dinner. The paper mentions that

[59] *Huddersfield Chronicle - 25/03/1871*

[60] *Huddersfield Chronicle - 27/04/1872*

[61] *Huddersfield Chronicle - 04/02/1881*

[62] *Leeds Times - 12/08/1882*

[63] *Huddersfield Examiner - 14/08/1885*

grouse was served and remarks on the miraculous way in which the birds, which could not legally have been shot prior to that day, had become so very tender!

The most serious accident in this period was the breaking of the connecting rod of a Manchester-bound train in the tunnel in September 1888, which pierced the boiler and resulted in the scalding of the engine crew with the subsequent death of the driver.[64] A final mention in the Press of the works which would lead to the building of the final tunnel, referred to the letting of a contract in March 1889 for the widening to four tracks of the Slaithwaite - Marsden section of the line.[65]

It will be seen from the above, that the Canal Tunnel in particular had fallen from the public view, but what of canal traffic? In 1893 there was a lengthy Parliamentary enquiry into Canal Rates and Charges, which looked into the recent history of the Huddersfield Canal in particular. In November, the Huddersfield Chronicle reported on the evidence of local witnesses.[66]

Mr Stephen Yates, a Wakefield canal carrier, said that he formerly carried large quantities of malt from Mirfield and Wakefield to Manchester by way of the Huddersfield Canal, but in 1885 that traffic had ceased on account of the high tolls charged by the LNWR. James Brierley, a canal boat owner at Slaithwaite, spoke of the frequent stoppages on the canal, and said that the traffic had greatly decreased of late years. Mr Swindells, General Manager of the Calder & Hebble Navigation stated that 75,000 ton of traffic was exchanged with his canal (at Cooper Bridge), but that only 14,332 ton of this went beyond Huddersfield due to prohibitory rates and frequent stoppages – much of this was probably coal traffic to mills on the east side. John Sugden of Folly Hall, a Drysalter, said that he formerly obtained his materials by

---

[64]   *Yorkshire Post - 29/09/1888*
[65]   *Huddersfield Chronicle - 16/3/1889*
[66]   *Huddersfield Chronicle - 09/11/1893*

canal from Manchester but had been driven off by the high rates. There appears to be plenty of evidence to suggest that the railway company was deterring traffic. At the conclusion of the enquiry there seems to have been a brief hope that the company would be forced to lower their rates, but finally, the LNWR seems to have lobbied successfully and the situation was allowed to continue. Their argument appears to have been that the canal was much more expensive to maintain than other nearby canals and that a much higher toll was therefore justified, but this seems academic if the tolls charged resulted in there being no traffic to pay them. Following the failure of this enquiry to reduce the rates charged, the eventual fate of the canal was inevitable.

Figure 26 - A detail from an early photograph of Tunnel End showing the portals of the First (Nicholson - at the centre) and Second (Nelson - at the left) single track railway tunnels. The fresh ballast under the twin tracks in the foreground suggest the picture was taken in the mid 1890s.

5
The Third Railway Tunnel 1890 - 1894

The construction of the third, double track, railway tunnel at Standedge was included in the LNWR (Additional Powers) Act of 1888, which covered a number of lines across the country. In railway days it was often called the North Tunnel, with the others being referred to as the Up and Down South Tunnels ('Up' being the Nelson Tunnel and 'Down' the Nicholson. This is based on the whole line being notionally east - west; as the tunnels actually run only 40 degrees off north-south, 'up' being towards London on the LNWR system.) The powers to build the tunnel were to lapse if not completed in five years, which probably explains why a new Act had been necessary when the second tunnel was built.

Work appears to have started in August 1890 with work on Redbrook New Shaft, using directly-employed labour, followed by the new shaft

(c) Kirklees Museums & Galleries

Figure 27 - Navvy huts at Tunnel End, Marsden with the reservoir in the background.

at Brun Clough on 26th September, but serious work on the tunnel proper does not seem to have started until 28th November, when a local diary records *"first shot fired in tunnel."*[67] Accommodation for the workers was provided in the form of wooden huts close to the ends of the Tunnel and at the shaft sites on Standedge Moor. There were no less than 54 proposed at Marsden, located at New Ing and Tunnel End.[68] The problem with the siting of the huts at both ends is that it involved men who had consumed more drink than was safe in the local village walking back along the canal towpath and as work progressed a number of reports appear in the press of men being drowned at both Marsden and Diggle. [69] [70] [71] [72] [73]

Work on the shafts included enlarging Cote Pit and Pule and a third new shaft at Flint Pit. Not all went well though, with a pumping engine falling 55 ft. down the new Redbrook shaft in November 1890.[74] The new Brun Clough shaft had to be abandoned in July 1891 due to problems with the amount of water entering the shaft and it was then decided to enlarge the existing shaft instead.[67]

At the start of 1891, the first fatality occurred, when a man was killed by a landslip at Marsden.[75] Another man was injured in the same

[67] *Geoff Brown notes. The local diary was of John Holroyd, transcribed by the Marsden Historical Society. Unfortunately, some of the sources available to Geoff in the 1970's and 1980's, for instance when he interviewed people still living who could remember the works, are no longer available. He did some work towards creating the Kirklees Sound Archive..*

[68] *Huddersfield Chronicle - 04/10/1890*

[69] *Huddersfield Chronicle - 16/02/1891 (Man drowned at Diggle)*

[70] *Huddersfield Weekly Examiner - 07/02/1891 (Marsden Local Board discussed the need for a lamp by the gate to the towpath after another man was drowned)*

[71] *Oldham Standard - 16/02/1891 (Man drowned at Diggle)*

[72] *Mossley & Saddleworth Reporter - 06/06/1891 (Body recovered from canal. "Heavy drinker," but verdict "Suicide")*

[73] *Huddersfield Weekly Examiner - 21/11/1891*

[74] *Huddersfield Weekly Examiner - 22/11/1890*

[75] *Oldham Chronicle - 03/01/1891*

incident and later died. In February another man was injured by the collapse of a crane and later died.[76]

This was apparently a time of depression in the coal industry and many Welsh miners were recruited, so many that Wrigley Mill Methodist Chapel started Welsh services, which was reported in February 1891.[77] Around 600 men were now working.

In February, work was started on sinking Flint Pit New Shaft. This also would be afflicted by excess water, a problem that was only solved by drilling a hole down into the Canal Tunnel to allow it to drain away. However, a number of local farms lost their water supply.[67] There were frequent reports in the local press about damage to roads and tipping of debris, particularly in Marsden. In October, it was reported that the LNWR had built a privy at Rough Lee on a site *"offensive to public decency!"*[78]

Figure 28 - A view across Standedge Moor with Flint Pit New Shaft in the foreground, Flint Pit (canal) behind and the Redbrook Engine House in the distance. The brown patch between the canal shaft and the Engine House marks the remains of Heathy Lee main shaft.

[76]   *Huddersfield Weekly Examiner - 12/02/1891*
[77]   *Mossley & Saddleworth Reporter - 07/02/1891*
[78]   *Huddersfield Weekly Examiner - 03/10/1891*

A newspaper report in December 1891 mentions the completion of the first section of brickwork, the first bricks having been laid 1½ miles in from Diggle on the 30th November by the wife and young son of the Engineer, Mr A A Macgregor.[79] They were later presented with a silver trowel and a silver mug to commemorate the event. At this time the heading from Diggle was 2 miles in, progress from the Marsden end having been slowed by a lack of space to tip the spoil at that end. No less than 40 working faces are mentioned and boats were being used to remove much of the spoil. It was hoped that the heading and shafts would be complete by the coming Easter. The report also mentions the piling works to extend the Canal Tunnel at the Diggle end and the demolition of the old canal bridge and lockhouse (possibly the tunnel-keeper's house, as the first lock is some distance from the works?)

In March 1892, Redbrook New Shaft was completed along with work to widen the old shaft at Brun Clough and by April the tunnel was

Figure 29 - A view at Tunnel End, Marsden during the construction of the third railway tunnel; note the iron boats on the canal being used to remove much of the spoil.

[79] *Huddersfield Chronicle - 11/12/1891*

headed throughout. There were stirrings of industrial action due to working conditions.[80] Shortly afterwards, there was a Mayday parade around the Marsden area of around 40 horses involved in the tunnel works.[81] On the return journey from the Great Western Inn, one of the men fell beneath the wheels of a cart, breaking his thigh. The paper does not mention whether drink was a factor, but it does say that he was taken to the site hospital in Waters Road and attended by the resident doctor, which gives an indication of the progress in such matters since the earlier tunnels were dug. However, the doctor was of no use in the case of Thomas Jones, who was killed by a fall down Redbrook shaft in April.[82]

In October 1893 there is a mention of the Standedge Tunnel Church Mission, when the organisers, Mr & Mrs Holt, moved away and a presentation of a *"five o'clock tea service"* was made to them.[83] The Mission had probably been established around May 1892, at the same time as a similar establishment at Diggle and this would certainly have helped to relieve pressure on the local churches, though other facilities were also under pressure.[83] The number of pupils at Kiln Green School in Diggle had increased from 60 to 160 and the local postal service was suffering a serious overload.[84]

Later in 1892, as the tunnel was being enlarged to its full size, the dumping of spoil continued to be a problem and a legal action was mounted to prevent the Company using the Marsden cricket ground for tipping.[85] This must have been resolved fairly quickly, as by February work was proceeding on a new cricket ground behind the Old New Inn, where the present Marsden football ground is sited. The former cricket ground was located in the area that became the station goods yard,

[80]   *Mossley and Saddleworth Reporter - 09/04/1892, 16/04/1892 and 23/04/1892*
[81]   *Huddersfield Chronicle - 10/05/1892*
[82]   *Mossley and Saddleworth Reporter - 23/04/1892*
[83]   *Huddersfield Chronicle - 07/10/1893 also*
       Mossley and Saddleworth Reporter - 07/05/1892
[84]   *Mossley and Saddleworth Reporter - 19/03/1892*
[85]   *Huddersfield Chronicle - 29/10/1892 and 21/02/1893*

Lock 39E

Warehouse Hill

Lock 40E

MARSDEN

Lock 42E

Tunnel End

Tunnel End
Reservoir

Figure 30 - A Google Earth® view from 2009 of the Marsden and Tunnel End area. The tinted overlays indicate the extent of tipping of spoil form the third railway tunnel.

today a car park. Much material must have been tipped in this area between the top four locks at Marsden and the railway, as well as on the opposite side of the canal, which as a result today is in what appears to be a shallow cutting between Locks 40E and 42E. Any facilities the canal may have had on the offside of the canal at Warehouse Hill above Lock 39E are likely to have disappeared at this time.

During November 1892, the new shaft at Flint Pit was finished and sadly, another death occurred, when a man who had been working in the Canal Tunnel was struck by a train at Diggle.[86]

In early 1893 there are several references to smallpox in the navvy accommodation.[87] There was a problem with navvies moving from one site to another and bringing the disease with them. In May, another death occurred, when the Foreman of the Pony Drivers was trapped between wagons at the Diggle end of the Tunnel.[88] It was becoming apparent that it would take longer to build this tunnel than the Nelson Tunnel and in July 1893, the LNWR obtained an extension of the time allowed. Three further years were allowed in this new Act.

In April 1894, there was a serious roof fall near to the Diggle end in a section not yet lined, when timbers 20 inches in diameter were broken. Fortunately it occurred a few hours before work resumed after the Easter holiday. Finally, in June 1894, the last brick was laid, and at the beginning of August the Board of Trade inspected the work. The Huddersfield Chronicle announced that the first train would pass through on the evening of Sunday 5th August and that the two single line tunnels would then close for three months for repairs.[89] The work had taken almost exactly four years and had consumed 120 ton of gelignite and 25 million bricks.

---

[86]   *Oldham Chronicle 19/11/1892*
[87]   *Oldham Chronicle 24/12/1892, Mossley and Saddleworth Reporter 18/03/1893, 15/04/1893*
[88]   *Mossley and Saddleworth Reporter 13/05/1893*
[89]   *Huddersfield Chronicle 03/08/1894*

Diggle

Present day
Canal Tunnel portal
(dated 1893)

Figure 31 - A Google Earth® view from 2012 of the Diggle area indicating, by the dotted line, the Canal Tunnel extension that was required for the building of the twin track railway, in use today.

Because the new railway tunnel was built on the north side of the Canal Tunnel, the railway needed to cross the canal at either end. This was achieved just inside the Canal Tunnel at the Marsden end, but the Canal Tunnel had had to be extended by 242 yd at the Diggle end, where two platforms of the rebuilt Diggle station actually stood above the new section. According to Geoff Brown's researches this was a <u>net</u> extension, as he believed that a short length of the Canal Tunnel was first opened out and then covered over.

The Canal Tunnel had had to be closed for part of the time that the new tunnel was being cut: from 4th September to 19th December 1892; 20th March to 10th April 1893, and again from 10th June when the railway company announced that it would be closed for six months. During that time a small number of traffics would be carried by rail:

Figure 32 - A Huddersfield to Manchester train emerges from the Diggle Portal.

grain, from Huddersfield to Stalybridge for Buckley & Newton; acid, from Huddersfield to Greenfield for Holliday & Sons; bricks and undressed stone from Linthwaite to Mossley for the Executors of John Walker. Buckley & Newton had their own boats, but the other two traffics had probably been carried by contractors. Significantly, the Huddersfield Chronicle article about the completion of the railway tunnel also revealed that about 400 men were then employed in repairs to the Canal Tunnel. Anyone who has been through the Canal Tunnel and seen the extent of the brick arching installed to repair blasting damage will appreciate the extent of the work involved. For some reason, the new tunnel had been built even closer to the Canal Tunnel than the first railway tunnel, despite the increased power of the explosives used and the knowledge of the damage done previously.

It would be 6th September 1894 before the Canal Tunnel re-opened, the six months closure having expanded to around fifteen.

Figure 33 - Brick jack arching installed to repair blast damage in the Canal Tunnel.

Figure 34 - As was customary, a commemorative Silver Trowel was presented on the completion of major engineering works with a celebratory dinner for the managers involved. This evocative portrait marks the completion of the North Tunnel and dinner at the Great Western PH on Standedge Moor. It is tempting to infer that the 'trowel' is being held by the lead engineer, Mr A A Macgregor.

Geoff Brown Collection

- 65 -

6
Standedge Tunnel, the Tunnel Book and After
1894 to Date

The Standedge Tunnel Book is a record of passages through Standedge Tunnel, from its re-opening in 1894 after the completion of the third railway tunnel.[90] It runs until the second World War (WW2), though there is only a handful of passages after the first World War, consisting mainly of pioneer private cruisers. The book records the dates and times of passages and ownership of boats, with Marsden - Diggle on the left page and Diggle - Marsden on the right, though there are a number of instances where the entries are transposed, probably due to the first entry being placed top left regardless. Sadly, it does not give any information on cargoes, the names of boats or those on board.

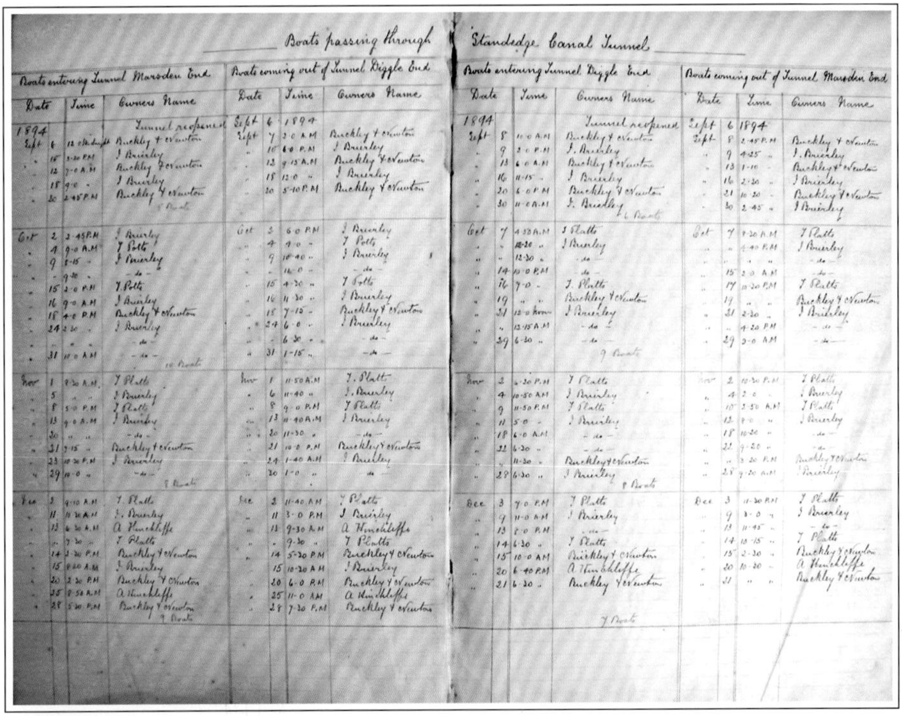

Figure 35 - The first pages of the Standedge Tunnel Book.

[90]   *Held in the National Waterways Archives at Ellesmere Port.*

The three surviving traffics through the Tunnel, which had been carried by rail during the closure period, were all to canalside locations from canalside locations and would have required multiple handling to carry by railway. Buckley and Newton, the corn millers of Stalybridge, who were situated just below what is now Lock 7W, had their own boats and were the first to use the Canal Tunnel immediately when it re-opened at midnight on 6th September 1894, although whoever made the entry seems to have placed it in the wrong column, suggesting that it started from Marsden.

Buckley and Newton are the carriers most easy to study and they account for 25% of all passages after the Tunnel re-opened. We know that they carried grain westwards and were usually empty in the other direction, though a small number of the times recorded might suggest that this was not always the case. We also know that they carried to their mill in Stalybridge. It would seem that the trips can not all have been to and from Huddersfield as the time between leaving and re-entering the Tunnel in one case is less than an hour and in another only three hours, possibly suggesting the collection of some cargo from

Arthur Cooke

Figure 36 - 'Umbria' loading at the Hardy Fertiliser Co.'s Mill below Lock 5W in Stalybridge.

Marsden, possibly from the railway-linked warehouse which formerly stood above the narrows below Lock 42E, though the timing of less than an hour is problematic even then and may be an error. However, there is a regular pattern of boats returning to the Tunnel in between 22 and 26 hours, still good going for around 15 miles and 84 locks to Huddersfield and back, and a smaller number around 14 - 16 hours, possibly suggesting a visit to the mill in Slaithwaite. Though we can not be sure of loading times, and weekends, when the mills would be closed, extending some trips. Later trips seem to be always in the longer time band.

Their times for the Tunnel passages average around 2½ hours eastbound (probably empty), with a couple of times equalling the long-supposed 'record' of 1 hour 20 minutes and two recorded at an hour exactly, which does stretch credibility a little. On the other hand, there are a few recorded as a 'mind-numbing' eleven hours, possibly due to low water levels. The average loaded time, going west, is around 4 hours, with only the odd one quicker than 2½ hours. There seems to have been considerable pressure at times to complete as many trips as possible. On Christmas Eve 1896 an eastbound boat passed through the Tunnel between 2.20 am and 4.30 am, presumably to load before a Christmas closure at the loading point, returning on Christmas Day. At times, the number of trips would also make it likely that more than one boat was involved, unless the crews were working 24 hours a day.

Other major carriers were James Brierley of Slaithwaite (45% of total), between 1894 and 1905 and Abraham Hinchcliffe (15%), between 1894 and 1902. Brierley was possibly associated with another of the traffics transferred to railway during the closure, that of stone from the wharf at Linthwaite, just above Lock 17E, to Mossley. There are a number of problems with entries for Brierley, probably because his boats often worked in pairs and the person making the entries has sometimes not recorded the second boat in one direction - this is hard to prove when a number of firms were using the Tunnel, but becomes more obvious as traffic declines. There is a case in August 1902 where such an error has been corrected, resulting in entries being offset.

It is tempting to associate Hinchliffe with the acid traffic that was transferred to the railway, particularly in the light of his later association with J & E Morton, the chemical firm at Milnsbridge. However, it is a fact that Hinchliffe acquired his new narrowboat 'Gleaner' just as the Tunnel re-opened and that he ceased using the Tunnel in 1902, around the time that the LNWR's canal service ceased to be advertised. He was Aspley-based, so although this must remain speculation, he may have operated as their agent, carrying whatever traffic they required. Certainly no LNWR boats are recorded in the Tunnel Book and they had used agents to carry by canal on their behalf in the past as well as for their road carriage.

The only other carriers of significance recorded are J Potts & Son of Dukinfield and Albert Wood of Sowerby Bridge, both with about 5% of the total, though what cargoes they carried is not known and there does not seem to be a regular pattern to their trips.

The last regular traffic ceased with Buckley and Newton in April 1913. A few trips were made by Potts, Wood and James Hall of Droylsden until August, when all traffic ceased. Apart from a single, one-way passage by a boat owned by the Great Central Railway, possibly in transit from their works at Gorton to the Chesterfield Canal which they owned, nothing is recorded until 12 trips on behalf of J W Leitch & Co. of Milnsbridge, carrying acid, probably to Ratcliffe & Sons of Mossley, in 1916. This would appear to be the final commercial traffic through the Tunnel. It is often stated that the last loaded trip was a passage by a boat belonging to J & E Morton of Milnsbridge in November 1921, but this is one-way trip and is almost certainly the importing of a boat called 'Mary Ann', which was registered at Mirfield in early March 1922, probably after some work at a local boatyard.

After a lengthy period, on 25th August 1932, at 2.00 pm, *"Woodward's Motor Boat"* is recorded entering, ostensibly at Marsden *(but see below)* at 12.30 pm and leaving at 2.00 pm. 'Mr Woodward' remains a mystery, but he was probably the first of a small group of private cruisers who made the trip in the 1930s.

"Carr-Ellison" is recorded on 21st July 1934, again at Marsden *(but again, see below)*. Captain Carr-Ellison was a military man and a member of a Northumbrian land-owning family, who still own extensive estates near Alnwick. An article appeared about him in "Canal Boat" Magazine April 1997, though sadly with not much information about his Huddersfield trip. Though there are *'ditto'* marks under the words *"motor boat"* in the Tunnel Book, according to that article he would probably have been using the steam launch *'Thetis'* in 1934. Carr-Ellison had started his cruising career in 1930 with a trip from the River Thames to Ripon in an open 12 ft launch, so he certainly would not have had any concerns about tackling the Tunnel.

The final trip prior to WW2 was by a Mr or Dr Greene - he is styled in one way going through the Tunnel and the other on return. Greene appears to have been a Gloucester doctor who owned a converted narrowboat called *'Success'*. He also seems to have been a self-publicist as his attempt to reach Huddersfield from Gloucester was recorded in a number of local newspapers as he progressed. In fact

Figure 37 - Mr/Dr Greene's 'Success' on the canal at Marsden, shown in this rather poor image.

he abandoned the attempt at Marsden due to a lack of time. In the Tunnel Book, Greene is recorded as entering the Tunnel at <u>Marsden</u> at an unreadable time on 20th August 1937 and leaving it at 1.20 pm *(in one of the newspaper reports, he claimed 1 hour 40 minutes for the passage)*, then entering at <u>Diggle</u> 10.00 am on 21st and leaving at 12.00 noon. It is obvious that the Tunnel Book entries are in the wrong columns, presumably due to a natural tendency to make the first entry on the left, Marsden, page. This must put a question mark against the other entries on that page, for both Woodward and Carr-Ellison. The entry for Greene is the last in the Tunnel Book, and *"nil"* is entered for each year up until 1942.

One period of the history where Geoff Brown was able to interview people with knowledge was WW2. Although the Canal Tunnel had long ceased to be a route for freight, it was thought in 1939 that the railway tunnels might be vulnerable to sabotage and the local Duke of Wellington's Regiment (TA) were given the task of guarding not just the two ends, but the shafts. A detachment was stationed in the warehouse at Tunnel End, where signs of their occupation were still clearly visible prior to restoration. The task of standing guard at, for example, Pule shaft, in all weathers, through the winter of 1939/40,

Trevor Ellis

Figure 38 - Concrete hut near Flint New Pit.

can only be imagined. Today the only remaining sign of military occupation is thought to be the small concrete hut at Flint New Pit, though this was not constructed in time for the initial period, when according to Geoff's interviewees, they were under canvas. The base of what was probably another hut remains at Pule. After April 1940, the local Home Guard inherited the thankless task.[91]

Apart from a short length in Huddersfield up to Lock 3E, the canal was legally closed under an Act of 1944 which the London Midland and Scottish Railway (LMS) used to dispose of its responsibility to maintain a number of canals. At first this had little impact on the canal and some new lock gates were installed, though the only use was by maintenance boats in order to maintain the canal for water supply purposes, this being the major remaining source of income in the days when the textile industry was a customer on both sides of the hill.

The last known trip through the canal is a passage by the founders of the Inland Waterways Association (IWA) in 1948. Since WW2, the IWA had achieved some success in the Midlands and elsewhere by using the right of navigation included in many Canal Acts to compel their owners to make improvements and they decided on a northern campaign. The two founders, Robert Aickman and Tom Rolt have both left accounts of the trip, which differ greatly, possibly because of their subsequent bitter disagreement and a desire on the part of each not to mention the other.[92] Rolt's account is the more detailed and it suggests that their boat, a converted ship's lifeboat called *'Ailsa Craig'*, became fast, probably in the worst of the narrows close to Redbrook and was only able to pass when he broke off some wooden strips from the cabin top and then drove the boat at full speed into the narrow section. Their campaign, although well-intentioned, was, in retrospect, a

---

[91] *Geoff Brown wrote articles for the Huddersfield Examiner, which were published 11/04/1988, 15/09/1988 and 20/09/1988.*
[92] *Aickman, R., The River Runs Uphill (1986). J M Pearson*
Rolt, L.T.C., Landscape with Canals (1977). Sutton Publishing Ltd

Figure 39 - 'Ailsa Craig' ready to enter Standedge Tunnel at Diggle with the founders of the IWA.

mistake as there was no right of navigation on the canal due to it having been legally abandoned. The owners had been retaining it in a barely navigable state for maintenance reasons, but the trip caused the *(now nationalised)* owners a lot of trouble and was probably one reason for the removal of the lock gates on both sides of the canal in 1950.

The Canal Tunnel still had to be maintained and a boat, thought to be Abram Hinchliffe's *'Gleaner'*, which came to the then Docks and Inland Waterways Executive (DIWE) - later the British Waterways Board (BWB) - via J & E Morton and the LMS, was retained at Marsden for maintenance. Ironically, according to an article in the Yorkshire Post, as *"LMS no. 7"*, it had been one of the two boats used to remove the gates and had had to be returned to Marsden by lorry.[93] Renamed *'Marsden'*, the boat was also used to continue a tradition of giving occasional trips through the Tunnel for interested groups by the DIWE and their successors, sometimes as part of an inspection. It was apparently fitted with a pump to create a form of jet drive and

---

[93]   *Yorkshire Post and Leeds Intelligencer - 06/09/1950*

thus avoided the need for legging or shafting.[94] The last of these trips appears to have been in the late 1960s when, according to Geoff Brown, a certain canal society complained about the standards, in particular the lighting, and the engineer in charge promptly discontinued such trips. In the 1970s there were reports of rock falls in the Tunnel, which would have put an end to these activities in any case.

A number of inspection trips were subsequently made into the Tunnel and some work was done by way of shoring and repairs, but British Waterways (BW) became very secretive about the Tunnel and its condition, possibly partly because of the formation, in 1974, of the Huddersfield Canal Society, who saw it as the canal's major asset and were agitating for access to the Tunnel as part of their campaign for restoration of the canal. As a result, the next known trip by a member of the public was completely unauthorised, when in 1979 Robin Witter, noted for his exploration of a number of the disused canal tunnels in the UK, canoed the Tunnel from Marsden to Diggle, taking photographs, some of which were published in "Waterways World" in March 1980.

The official reaction to this publicity was to attempt to increase security, but as the canal began to be restored in the 1980s and 1990s, there was a realisation that the issue would have to be faced and towards the end of this period a limited number of trips took place with interested parties from the Joint Committee set up by the local authorities and potential funders. Finally, in 1997, it was announced that the restoration had secured Millenium funding.

Work on the Tunnel commenced in May 1999, with extensive desilting, continuing with rock bolting works; the worst sections being covered with mesh and spray concrete.

The first boats passed through on 1st May 2001 and an official re-opening ceremony took place on 3rd September, when HRH Prince of Wales visited Tunnel End.

---

[94]   *Yorkshire Post and Leeds Intelligencer - 09/09/1954*

Figure 40 - Rock bolting works in Standedge Tunnel.

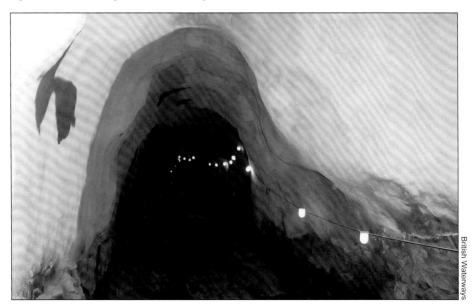

Figure 41 - An unstable section of Standedge Tunnel reinforced by spraying concrete on to a stainless steel mesh support..

The initial arrangements for taking boats through the Tunnel were heavily influenced by Health and Safety concerns, including doubts about ventilation and possible access by boaters to the railway tunnels. It was decided that an arrangement would be put in place to tow private boats through using electric tugs; all members of the public riding in a 'Passenger module'. This was never a happy arrangement, with many reports of damage to boats and the question of liability in such cases. Some of the additional features put in hand, such as the use of rubber sheeting to protect boats, caused their own problems with damage to paintwork by grit picked up on the sheets.

Figure 42 - Positioning an inflatable buffer or 'jebus' between the boats in readiness for towing through Standedge Tunnel.

Finally, in 2009, a new system was introduced whereby boaters were allowed to take their own boats through the Tunnel, accompanied by a 'Chaperone' providing they were prepared to abide by strict Health and Safety requirements. The title 'Chaperone' was presumably used because the term 'Pilot' has legal implications of responsibility for the boat and the 'Chaperone' is there purely for advisory and Health and Safety reasons. Standedge Tunnel will always be different from the other tunnels on the canal network due to the length of the passage, the tightness of some of its narrower sections, the problems of ventilation and potential access to a live railway tunnel.

However, the present system is expensive in terms of staff used, requiring a Tunnel Controller, who monitors progress of boats by means of telecommunications as they progress through the Tunnel from four 'Safety Adits', which have been equipped with lighting and telecommunications. With a Tunnel Chaperone on each boat, at present a maximum of three each way on three days a week, this can take five people to operate, including a person nominated to access the disused Nicholson Tunnel in an emergency.

Figure 43 - A convoy of boats emerging at Tunnel End having been towed through the Tunnel by BW's tug and passenger module in 2003.

ANNEXES

Annex 1: Developments at Tunnel End, Marsden

Geoff Brown compiled a report for BW, which appears to date from the late 1980s or early 1990s. It was concerned mainly with the history of Tunnel End reservoir and spillway and may have been connected with the proposals being made around that time to make the reservoir comply with current legislation. The information here which relates to the reservoir is drawn largely from that report.

Tunnel End Reservoir is an original feature of the canal, being shown on the map produced by Nicholas Brown for the original meeting of subscribers in 1793. It appears in the Canal Company Minutes in December 1797, when it was minuted that work should start on building it, and by October 1798 the Committee were urging William Bayliffe to finish it, as the canal to Marsden was then nearing completion.

The Canal Company was constrained by provisions in the Act of Parliament to protect the interests of mill owners in the Colne Valley, most mills at that time being water-powered. As a consequence, a goit was constructed which bypassed the Reservoir, running along the side nearest to Waters Road from the head of the Reservoir to near the dam, where it disappeared underground and turned down the field towards the canal, which it crossed parallel to the footbridge. It can be traced on the far side by the boarded section on the footbridge ramp, which hides a shaft down to the culvert. It then crosses beneath the railway lines to join the river just below the outlet of the reservoir spillway. At some point in its route down the field, the goit must have crossed another culvert, which was the feeder from the reservoir to the canal. This started from a valve set into the reservoir bank, now buried, and emerged into the canal on the outside of the sharp bend just east of the footbridge; this feeder has been out of use for many years.

The Reservoir has always been prone to silting, and the first reports came early in the railway era, in 1849. A report which Geoff Brown traced in the then British Rail Archives stated *"Tunnel End Reservoir is*

*rapidly filling with wreck and gravel and where there was once
12 ft. of water when the reservoir was first constructed it is now level
with the gauge weir."* What was done about the problem at that time
was not recorded, but with that rate of silting, it seems safe to assume
that dredging must have taken place then, and possibly on at least one
more occasion before the next record in 1915 *(see page 92).*

One peculiarity of the building of the reservoir is that the Parish
boundary between 'Marsden in Huddersfield' and 'Marsden in
Almondbury' had been the course of the river. This was not altered and
on subsequent maps it is possible to trace the former course of the river
from this boundary, which meanders along the reservoir and across
the Tunnel End area. On the 1852 OS map, it crossed the canal at the
footbridge.

A feature which has changed frequently is the reservoir spillway. This
was probably the fundamental reason for Geoff Brown being asked to
compile his report, as there was increasing doubt about the adequacy of
the spillway to deal with a major flood and the Reservoirs Act of 1975
brought pressure on BWB, forerunners of BW and the Canal and River
Trust (CRT), as owners. A number of proposals were made around this
time and it would appear that they were keen to know the full history of
the site, particularly the history of ownership, which had been greatly
complicated by the separation of canal and railway after over a hundred
years of joint ownership.

As part of the report, Geoff Brown traced the development of the
spillway, which is shown below, derived from his original drawings.

While the initial layout *(Figure 44)*, with its straight spillway to the east
of the cottages and passing under the canal by an aqueduct, was well
before the age of photography, it was illustrated on the face of a watch
presented to Thomas Bourne, the 'Standedge Admiral' on his retirement
in 1848, which is in the possession of his descendants.

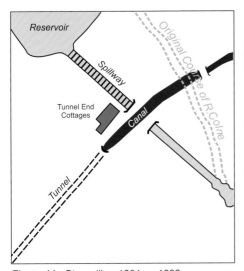

Figure 44 - Stage (i) c.1801 - c.1822

Figure 45 - Detail of the watch presented to Thomas Bourne.

In 1822, the Committee took the decision to divert the overflow over the tunnel mouth *(Figure 46)*. The Minutes of that meeting do not give any reason for the change, but the report to the next Annual Meeting does mention that a flood, which had occurred just prior to the decision to change the overflow, had caused serious damage to the reservoir bank. Elsewhere, Geoff calculated that the tunnel had been extended by 11 yd at this time, which would mean that the tunnel mouth as it stands must be of that date, rather than dating from the original opening of the tunnel, though the rebuild may have reused the original materials. Sadly, there do not appear to be any illustrations prior to the construction of the final railway tunnel which might show what the full façade looked like and also to explain the blocked opening to the right of the tunnel mouth.

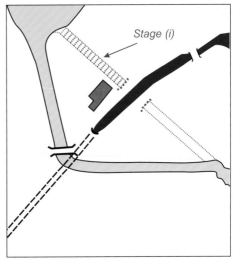

Figure 46 - Stage (ii) c.1822 - 1848

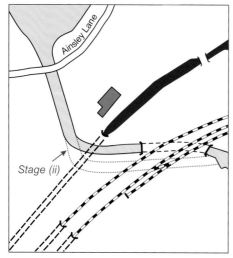

Figure 47 - Stage (iii) 1848

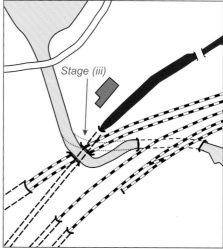

Figure 48 - Stage (iv) 1894 - Present Day

In 1848, with the construction of the first railway tunnel, the spillway was altered, in order to pass beneath the railway *(Figure 47)*.
The photograph below, which must have been taken prior to 1890, shows the spillway dropping down to pass beneath the railway.

Geoff Brown Collection

Figure 49 - Old photograph showing the spillway prior to the building of the double track railway.

Early in the construction of the final railway tunnel, the spillway assumed its present form *(Figure 48)*. First, an aqueduct was built to carry it over the entrance to the new tunnel, followed by a sharp elbow in order to resume its course beneath the tracks into the single-line tunnels. This sharp bend was where the spillway breached in the flood of 1946.[95] Today the repairs in concrete, with added buttresses, may still be seen; these were supposed to be a temporary 'fix', but over seventy years later are still in place. George Holroyd, who was Ganger at the time, was interviewed at length by Geoff Brown in the 1980s and said that the breach was caused by a large boulder which had been washed down. It narrowly missed a platelayers' hut which stood nearby where several men were having their lunch break. They beat a swift retreat and escaped with a soaking. The boulder is supposed to be buried somewhere beneath the breach.

Figure 50 - A dramatic view of the consequence of the spillway breach of 1946; the single track lines hang over the erosion void. Note the white Platelayers' hut by the tunnel.

[95] *Huddersfield Examiner - 20 & 21/09/1946, Colne Valley Guardian - 27/09/1946, Yorkshire Post - 21/09/1946*

Moving away from the Reservoir and spillway to the warehouse, it would seem that the canal has suffered from the problem that affects all old structures, whereby visitors to an old castle, for example, are always told that the surviving room is that where the great events occurred. Thus, in some past histories, transhipment of goods to road during the period that the Canal Tunnel was being completed was said to have taken place at this warehouse at Tunnel End (and at the transhipment shed at Woolroad), because these were surviving structures. However, prior to the building of the third turnpike road over Standedge in the 1830s, Tunnel End was a backwater and even today would not be a suitable starting point for the carriage of heavy loads westwards. In fact the Report to the Annual Meeting for 1812 mentions that the section of canal between the Summit Lock and Marsden Warehouse *"until the tunnel became navigable.....was little used"* and that the locks therefore needed work to bring them up to standard. Clearly, transhipment of goods while the tunnel was being built was carried out at Warehouse Hill, above Lock 39E, which was far better placed both for Marsden itself and the then road network, in which the turnpike road passed on the south side of Pule Hill by way of Mount Road. The Warehouse Hill site has, however, suffered from the loss of buildings and the encroachment of the railway goods yard in the 1890s and today it is difficult to imagine it as the main site in Marsden for the handling of goods.

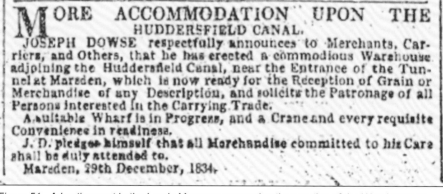

Figure 51 - Advertisement in the Leeds Mercury announcing the erection of the Warehouse at Tunnel End.

The existing warehouse at Tunnel End was constructed in the 1830s to serve Hey Green Corn Mill, which stood at the head of Tunnel End Reservoir and there is an announcement of its completion in the Leeds Mercury of 3rd January 1835. *(Figure 51)*

There was, formerly, a stone trackway which linked the mill to the warehouse. This trackway seems to have succumbed to damage by traction engines at the time of the work on the third railway tunnel, though a length survives as the driveway to Bank Side, the house behind the warehouse.[96]

At some stage the warehouse appears to have been extended at the end furthest from the canal, as a clear, straight joint can be seen on both sides. This extension was itself later altered to accommodate a railway siding running though the double doors on either side, as can be seen from the evidence of blocked window openings. The siding is present on the 1852 OS map and was thus constructed shortly after the railway opened. The corn mill appears to have closed in 1882, following which the warehouse became a 'Magnesia Works', owned by a firm of manufacturing chemists. In 1895 it was taken over as a canal

Bob Gough

Figure 52 - The warehouse at Tunnel End.

---

[96] *Huddersfield Weekly Examiner - 07/11/1891 (The article reported the breakage of 56 stones)*

maintenance depot, which purpose it served until the canal re-opened in 2001. The siding was still present during the building of the third railway tunnel, but is missing from the 1906 OS Map and may therefore have been lifted when those works ended.

Early maps show only the present cottages, with a much longer extension of stables at the end furthest from the tunnel, and another building in the area of the present car park, which, from early postcard views, was another cottage. The latter appears to have survived until after WW2. There are also references to an Inn, though it is hard to tell whether this may be the same as the later Junction Inn at the top of the lane. However, in the 1850s, the first OS map shows an L-shaped building or buildings on the side of the canal across the footbridge next to the winding hole. What these were is uncertain and they seem to have been short-lived, though they covered a similar area to the surviving warehouse. The only access to them appears to have been the footbridge and so they may have been cottages, possibly built to accommodate the signalmen and others needed for the operation of the original single-line tunnel. As such they may have become redundant when the second tunnel was opened, and certainly nothing appears on the plans of 1885 when the third tunnel was first proposed.

There is correspondence of the 1850s, which Geoff Brown had copied, written by Robert Carter, the Canal Manager, and involving Thomas Nicholson, to Joseph Brook of Greenhead. Brook had been Deputy Chairman of the Huddersfield and Manchester Railway and Canal Company (HMRCC) and was described in a Directory of 1848 as *"Deputy Chairman, London & North Western Railway (Huddersfield & Manchester Section)"*, which suggests that the HMRCC must at least briefly have operated as a separate entity within the LNWR. The letters are about the proposed construction of a goods yard and wharves, which seems to have involved the use of land between canal and river and between canal and railway, on the stretch between Marsden station and Tunnel End. The intention was for Nicholson to have his stone wharf in the area which later became Tunnel End sidings with a railway warehouse and wharf opposite between canal and railway. On an LNWR map, produced some time prior to the building of the third railway tunnel, but including later updates, all of this land is still described as *"Spoil Bank"*, which it remains today, so it appears nothing was ever done. However, a listing of wharves on the canal, compiled in 1927, but often referring back to a much earlier date, does refer to wharves existing on both sides of the canal at Tunnel End.

The earliest known photograph of the Tunnel End area *(Figure 49)* shows Stage (iii) of the spillway and therefore dates from the period prior to 1890, but no other illustrations of this period have been found. The next known photographs were taken near to the completion of the third railway tunnel around 1894 and, in addition to the later stages of the tunnel works, one shows a glimpse of a short-lived tramway which ran to Hey Green and crossed the canal on a flimsy-looking trestle bridge. It is thought to have been used to carry puddle-clay.

Figure 53 - Detail of Figure 29 showing a tramway from Hey Green crossing the canal at some height on a flimsy-looking trestle bridge.

The building of the third railway tunnel was accompanied by the provision of extensive hutted accommodation at both ends. A plan of around 1893 exists of the huts at Tunnel End, showing four along Ainsley Lane and a number in the field above. There is also a photograph in the Kirklees archive showing the latter *(Figure 27)*. Other buildings are shown on the plan along the lane down to Tunnel End and in the adjacent field. At this time there was still the railway siding into the warehouse, passing though the building into the yard and extensive sidings between canal and river on the far side of the railway, though the short-lived tramway crossing the canal is not shown. From his studies of the various plans, Geoff Brown deduced that the layout of the tracks was altered between planning and construction, with the curve at the end of the new tunnel being tightened so that the new tracks crossed the canal where the original railway crossing had been. This necessitated altering the ends of the old tunnels slightly to accommodate the curve and the building of a new crossing over the canal for these tracks, with the lines into the new tunnel using the original bridge.

Figure 54 - Detail of a postcard showing the wooden trestle viaduct crossing the River Colne.

Following the completion of the third railway tunnel, Tunnel End Sidings, between river and canal, took on a new rôle. Huddersfield Corporation were building Butterley Reservoir in the Wessenden Valley and had a need to import puddle clay for the dam. They obtained an Act of Parliament, dated 1894, for a standard-gauge railway from the sidings to the dam. This left the sidings at the end furthest from the tunnels, crossed the River Colne on a wooden trestle viaduct, then climbed steeply across the Manchester Road (A62), rounded the hillside to cross Old Mount Road and then across the fields to Hard End and the reservoir. Clay was brought from Mossley, necessitating a reversal at Marsden station to reach the sidings. The 1905 OS map shows a crossover close to Station Road bridge and what appears to be a run-round loop on the southern-most track. A small six-coupled saddletank, named 'Butterley', was bought for the line, and must have really earned its keep with the ascent from the sidings having a steepest gradient of 1 in 21 from the viaduct, a section at 1 in 62 and then five furlongs at 1 in 27. The line was not finally dismantled until 1907/8. Today there is little to be seen, presumably because of the requirement for reinstatement contained in the Act, although the stone abutment for the viaduct at the end of the former sidings area may still be traced.

Figure 55 - The six-coupled saddletank 'Butterley'.

A different kind of
railway came to the area
in 1915, when major
dredging works were
carried out at Tunnel
End Reservoir.[97]
A floating dredger
and a number of boats
were dragged from the
canal up the lane to the
reservoir. Boats loaded
by the dredger were
floated under the bridge
beneath Ainsley Lane to
a point near the sluice
gates where mooring
rings may still be seen.
They were unloaded by
a crane into a chute.

L & N W Railway Gazette

Figure 56 - Dredging works at Tunnel End reservoir

A 2' 6" narrow gauge railway crossed a staging over the canal at the
end of the Canal Tunnel to reach the bottom of this chute. A loop
and sidings were provided alongside the main railway, from which a
line joined the canal towpath, raised for the purpose, to pass beneath
the main line (additional staging widened the towpath beneath the
bridges). It then followed the towpath down to the site of the present
CRT compound between Locks 37E and 35E, which, by then, was the
nearest place where the material could be tipped. The line bypassed
the narrows below Lock 42E and again left the towpath at Lock 39E
to cross the road and follow the present track down to the tip. The
operation seems to have continued until 1918 and employed two
small locomotives 'Platelayer' and 'Kitchener'. Gradients on this
line reached 1 in 14, but at least the loaded operations were downhill,
though braking must have been a major problem on wet rails, which
given the material being carried must have been most of the time!

---

[97]   *Originally published in the "L.N.W.R. Railway Gazette"*

Figure 57 - A rare image of the locomotive 'Platelayer' at Tunnel End

Again, little remains – the mooring rings; the altered towpath, which now slopes up to the end of the winding hole at Tunnel End and back down; the odd arrangement of the towpath wall below the narrows

Figure 58 - The altered towpath sloping up to the end of the winding hole at Tunnel End. The courses of the original masonry block wall are progressively buried beneath the towpath.

between Locks 42E and 41E, which slopes down and turns a right angle; and some signs of tipping tracks in the woodland by Lock 35E. The last traces of the wooden staging on the towpath beneath the railway were only removed when the canal was restored.

Despite nearly three years of work, Tunnel End Reservoir was again heavily silted by the 1960s, probably aided by increased erosion of the moors. There was also a growing doubt about the adequacy of the spillway to deal with a major flood and the Reservoirs Act of 1975 brought further pressure. In 1984, a proposal was made which would have reverted to an overflow on a similar line to the original, but using concrete pipes beneath the canal. There were many objections to the plan; probably in part because it simply moved the effect of a flood downstream into Marsden, and despite revised proposals over the next few years, the scheme lapsed. Ultimately it was decided to drain the reservoir and to allow the silt to dry out, thus removing it from being classified as a reservoir under the Act. Today, it is a nature reserve.

By the turn of the 1980s, Tunnel End Cottages had been unoccupied for many years and they were one of two projects which attracted the attention of the Canal Society; one was the restoration of two locks in Uppermill with a view to running a trip boat and demonstrating the feasibility of restoration, the other was the creation of a museum and visitor centre. It was expected that one of the two projects would come to fruition and the Society was overstretched when both came to pass. In the event, the West Yorkshire County Council took over the repair of the cottages through a Community Programme scheme designed to relieve unemployment. The cottage furthest from the Tunnel became a base for their Countryside Rangers. Eventually Kirklees Council inherited the premises and the Society retired from the scene after a few years. Since the restoration of the canal, British Waterways and their successors, the CRT, have run the cottages as a base and a café.

The recent history of the warehouse is a particularly contentious subject, but I feel that the matter cannot be neglected and I can only give my personal assessment. In fact, prior to restoration of the canal, the Society had commissioned a number of studies which looked at the potential of the warehouse to become a visitor centre and this was a key, if not *the* key, part of the Millennium bid which succeeded in restoring the whole canal.[98] Unfortunately, what materialised was a rather generic attraction which could have been at home in any of BW's sites and said little about Standedge. A significant amount of money was invested in a boat lift, which was installed in the warehouse's internal dock. It was intended to raise trips boats to floor level and load passengers as part of their 'Standedge Experience', but it only operated briefly before being abandoned. The lift concept, which needed the boats to be able to turn in their own length to enter the dock, compromised the design of the tugs, making them far more complex than was needed to run the Tunnel Trips.

The Visitor Centre never really caught on with the local public, despite there being a will among the local management for it to succeed. Following one of several BW re-organisations, the east side of the Narrow Canal, complete with Tunnel and Visitor Centre, were parachuted into the Yorkshire Region, where all three things were unfamiliar to the management and it was not long before the decision was taken to close it. Fortunately for the future of the site, the Visitor Centre's integral position in the Millennium package meant that, if it closed, then the whole of the funding became due for repayment, and it was re-opened. At the time of writing, a pared-down and unstaffed compromise is in place; though the CRT and the current management have commissioned a study with a view to maximising visitor numbers and we can only hope that money is eventually found for something which truly interprets the local area and encourages people to make a return visit.

‒●‒

---

[98] *L&R Leisure plc (1989) The Standedge Experience – Final Report*
Brooke Miller Peden (1996) Standedge Experience – Final Report

Annex 2: Developments at Diggle

The Diggle end of the Tunnel has suffered many changes as a result of railway construction and it may be clearer to look at these in one place.

The original layout of the canal was not constrained by the railway as at present and consisted of two large basins, either side of an aqueduct across the Diggle Brook. One face of this aqueduct survives and may be seen from the bridge over the Diggle Brook at Kiln Green, though it is becoming increasingly obscured by vegetation and buildings. After the second basin, the canal then passed under a bridge carrying the road and entered the tunnel somewhere between where the present road bridge stands and the double track railway tunnel entrance. (*Figure 59*)

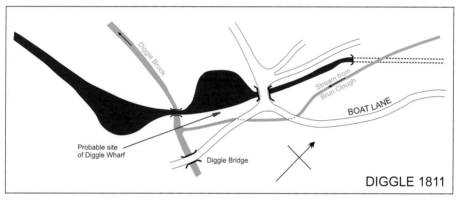

Figure 59

When the railway was first built, the course of the canal was straightened, and the two basins were left as ponds on the "wrong" side of the tracks. The plan (*Figure 60*) also shows it was probably necessary to first open out 37 yd of the original canal tunnel when the later extension was built in order to form the crossing for the two tracks and so the original tunnel entrance and the first few yards of the Tunnel no longer exist. This would indeed place the original entrance in an area somewhere midway between the present day road bridge and the double-track tunnel entrance and beneath the present tracks.

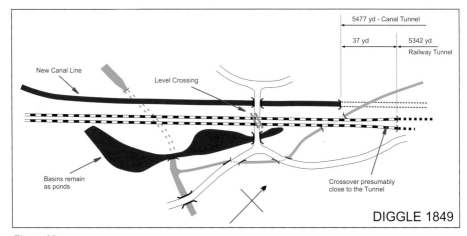

Figure 60

In 1852 a station opened at Diggle, just east of the level crossing indicated on the plan above, but there was to be little change to the basic layout, apart from the opening of the second tunnel, until the 1890s, when the third railway tunnel brought major changes. This is basically the state of the area in the old photograph of Diggle (*below*), though it would appear that an access had been made across the old canal, just to the west of the aqueduct.

Figure 61 - Detail of an early view of Diggle; probably the access was for the paper mill.

Figure 62 - A view of Diggle Station c.1900. Note the steam train emerging from the North Tunnel and the two single track portals to the right. The iron footbridge runs alongside the new road bridge, built to replace the level crossing.

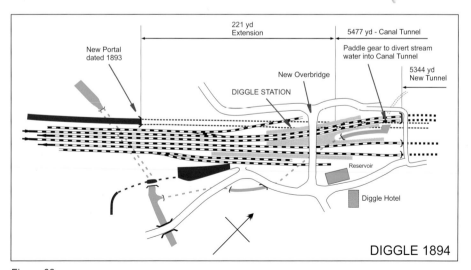

Figure 63

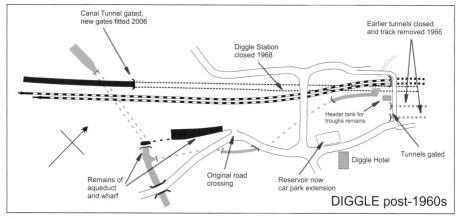

Figure 64

Canal Tunnel gated;
new gates fitted 2006

Earlier tunnels closed
and track removed 1966

Diggle Station
closed 1968

Header tank for
troughs remains

Tunnels gated

Diggle Hotel

Remains of
aqueduct
and wharf

Original road
crossing

Reservoir now
car park extension

DIGGLE post-1960s

By 1894, the construction of the Canal Tunnel extension and the greatly-extended Diggle station had removed the old canal bridge and much of the old canal had been infilled. The reservoir close to the Diggle Hotel was constructed to feed water troughs which were laid inside the three tunnels at this end to allow steam locomotives to pick up water without the need to stop. Such troughs were invented by John Ramsbottom of the LNWR in 1860 and were quickly installed

Figure 65 - An old postcard of Diggle looking up the valley. Note the extensive tips of tunnel debris around the mill and the 'dog-leg' in the canal.

Figure 66 - A fine view of Diggle Station in the late 1950s, taken from above the entrance to the Nelson Tunnel. Note the header tank for the water troughs and, behind the collection of sheds on the island platform, the channel for the Brun Clough stream, which has crossed the double tracks just out of shot to the right. Reproduced from: Wells, Jeffrey (1996). Miles Platting to Diggle. Challenger Publications

throughout their system. Although such troughs were common, this was the only such installation within a tunnel and was placed there because the tunnels were the only level track on this line. They extended for around 500 yd in the single tunnels and for around 560 yd in the later tunnel, where they were sited a little further from the entrance. The header tank for the troughs still exists between the double track tunnel and the two single track tunnels on what was the island platform of Diggle Station, though the reservoir marked on the plan *(Figure 63)* has been replaced by an extension to the car park of the Diggle Hotel.

These plans, re-drawn by Bob Gough, were originally created by Geoff Brown, probably in the 1990s, by which time the railway installations at Diggle were a shadow of their peak; *Figure 66* gives some indication of this past scene. Since then, the remains of the old canal have reduced still further and are normally dry, though the one remaining face of the aqueduct may still be seen *(Figure 67)*.

Figure 67 - A view from Kiln Green of the remaining face of the former aqueduct over Diggle Brook taken some years ago. Today this is partly obscured by vegetation and new buildings.

The Brun Clough stream is still visible, under the tracks outside the double track tunnel, crossing the Canal Tunnel in an iron trough. Today, there are few other remains associated with the canal in Diggle. The station is long closed and proposals to re-open it, which date from at least the 1980s, have come to nothing. Any replacement would probably be on a site away from the tunnels. Two houses which were built to replace those lost in the 1890s building works still exist, though much altered. One was probably the Tunnel Keeper's house, adjacent to the car park above the Tunnel extension, the other, the lock house at Lock 31W. As a result, there are few facilities associated with the Diggle end of the Tunnel, the only structure being a converted freight container which houses amenities for the Tunnel Chaperones.

There have been occasional short boat trips in from the Diggle end, which is actually the more interesting, with plenty of unlined rock beyond the extension, but these have been restricted to special events. However, the CRT currently offer through trips for the public at weekends.

Annex 3: Lengths of the Tunnels

The Canal Tunnel

The length of the Canal Tunnel has always been problematic.
There is clearly going to be some difficulty in producing a straight
line measurement in a tunnel which varies from its true line by as
much as 26 ft (7.9 m) using a surveyors chain. It is possible that some
measurement was done between shafts on the surface, and it may
be significant that one of the more consistent figures seen is for the
distance between Redbrook and Flint Pit, where there is a direct line of
sight and it would be possible to use a method such as triangulation.

Outram's original survey before the canal was built predicted a length
of 5451 yd (4984.4 m). This was revised to 5477 yd (5008.2 m) when
the pilot bore was completed and a direct measurement could be made.
Geoff Brown suggested that 32 yd (29.3 m) at the western end was
then opened out as the Tunnel was enlarged to its full size, resulting in
a final length of 5445 yd (4978.9 m) in the early operating years from
1811 to 1822.

Ove Arup

*Figure 68 - Distance plate 106 in the roof of the Tunnel. These plates were originally fixed at
50 yd intervals. Curiously, the numbering started from the original Diggle entrance to Marsden,
as opposed to the original numbering of the locks and milestones going in the opposite direction.*

In 1822, the position of the overflow at the Marsden end was moved from east of the cottages, where there was once an aqueduct *(see Annex 1 - Developments at Tunnel End)*, to run above the Tunnel entrance, and it is thought that 11 yd (10.1 m) were added at the Marsden end at this time, bringing the length to 5456 yd (4989.0 m).

Matters then rested until the 1890s and the building of the double-track railway tunnel, which resulted in the present Diggle portal with its date of 1893. It is thought that a further 32 yd (29.3 m) of Tunnel were first opened out between the original mouth of the Canal Tunnel and level with where the mouth of the new railway tunnel was to be, as the railway would need to cross over the canal. A covered extension of 274 yd (250.5 m) was then built, resulting in a net addition of 242 yd (221.3 m) to give a length of 5698 yd (5210.3 m).

At the time that Ove Arup carried out a survey prior to restoration, they gave the length as 5189.5 m (5675 yd), which differs by 23 yd (21.0 m) from the above figure. It is understood that they used a laser measuring system, but how they accounted for the "S-bend" is not known. Nonetheless, this is currently the accepted figure.

The Railway Tunnels

The lengths of the railway tunnels appear to be generally agreed at the present day, probably because it is possible to see through them and thus measure reliably. The two original tunnels are generally quoted as being 5342 yd (4884.7 m). The Nicholson Tunnel is approximately 50 ft (15 m) south of the Canal Tunnel with the Nelson Tunnel 25 ft (7.5 m) beyond, these figures being centre to centre, though of course the distance varies due to the wanderings of the Canal Tunnel.

The third railway tunnel is generally quoted as 5344 yd (4886.6 m). It is officially 55 ft (16.8 m) from the Canal Tunnel, again centre to centre, but given the 27 ft (8.2 m) span of the tunnel and the fact that the maximum deviation of the Canal Tunnel of some 26 ft (7.9 m) to the west of Redbrook is to this side, the minimum thickness of rock between the two could be as low as 10 ft (3.0 m) and it is hardly surprising that a long section of the Canal Tunnel to the west of the 'S-bend' is heavily-reinforced with the distinctive jack arches of the 1890s repairs.

Annex 4
The Shafts

The Shaft Depths

The original plan for the Canal Tunnel envisaged a total of 14 working shafts, which would be sunk down to canal level to allow work to be carried out in both directions. In addition, a number of other, shorter shafts would need to be dug to enable the construction of adits or soughs for water to run off into nearby streams, particularly at those sites where water balance engines were to be used. The remaining shafts are currently numbered from the Diggle/western end to Marsden in the east and the shafts will be described in that order. The following information relies heavily on the notes of Geoff Brown, who spent many years researching the tunnels.

If the story of the Tunnel's length is complicated, the question of the depths of its shafts is, if anything, worse. Firstly, as in the case of the length, estimates of depth were made at the time of the original survey, which were amended by actual measurement as soon as this was possible; a measurement from ground level at the top of the shaft to the bottom of the initial heading seems to have been used. However, as construction progressed, the shafts actually became deeper as the ground level was raised by the deposition of material around the shaft tops. Surveys after the Tunnel was enlarged to its finished size used the depth from the then ground level to where the shaft met the completed Tunnel. The difference between these figures and the earlier measurements will vary according to whether the shaft is in a lined section or rock and by the amount that the ground level had risen at each site.

In a much later a survey, conducted in 1925 in LMS railway days, it seems to have been the practice to measure from ground level to rail level, reflecting that company's primary interest and the fact that the Canal Tunnel was now disused. Oddly, given that the shafts are over the Canal Tunnel, there does not seem to be a case where the depth was measured to normal water level in the Canal Tunnel, though it may have been necessary to take this measurement first and adjust it to get a measurement to rail level.

All the open shafts have, or had, a wall constructed around the top, typically of around 12 to 15 ft (3.7 to 4.6 m) in height. Following the end of steam traction on the railway in the late 1960s, two of the shafts, Brun Clough and Redbrook New, had this wall lowered and were then capped in concrete. Most of the shafts which remained open and accessible were measured by Ove Arup & Co (Arup) using modern techniques in their survey of the 1990s prior to restoration. Judging from the figures given at Redbrook, where one shaft was measured to be several feet deeper than the other, they seem to have used a measurement from ground level to the absolute bottom of the shaft, in this case including the sump of what had been the pumping shaft.

The Shafts in Detail

Outram took advantage of the relatively gently rising ground at the Diggle end to construct six shafts in the first 938 yd (857.7 m). The first five working shafts at Diggle have all been infilled, though one or two of them reveal themselves by particularly wet patches of tunnel lining and some can be traced as small spoil heaps above ground. The sites of the first and second shafts were probably eliminated by the works on the later railway tunnel. Shafts four and five were never completed down to tunnel level, which brings the added complication that the 'Sixth pit' ('Cote Pit') was being referred to as the 'Fourth Pit' in the Canal Company Minutes around 1806.

What was originally known as the 'Sixth Pit,' later 'Fourth Pit', was also known as 'Diggle Edge', 'Tickler' or 'Tittlers', or 'Cote Pit' and is today's No.1 Shaft. Although all of these six shafts were started in the first couple of years of the works for the Canal Tunnel, around 1794-1796, this shaft was not finally completed until 1807. Today it is open, at a distance of 1,180 yd (1079.0 m) from the present Diggle entrance, but it may once have been infilled following the completion of the Canal Tunnel as it does not appear on a section which formed part of the plans for the first railway tunnel in 1844. In 1865, on a plan for the second tunnel, it was described as having *"Field, Old Engine House, Footpath, Stream and Shaft"*, but by 1887 on the plan for the third railway tunnel the old engine house has been replaced by *"Waste Heap"*, suggesting that tipping had buried the earlier remains.

As it stands today its state reflects its use in the construction of the final, north railway tunnel, when it was enlarged to a diameter variously quoted as 8 ft 6 in, 9 ft or 10 ft (2.5 m on the Arup survey, which tends to support the first figure) and lined in stone to a depth of 10.6 m (Arup), followed by brick to 23.0 m, below which it is unlined. It was surrounded by a 12 ft (3.5 m) brick wall, though this may have been lowered, judging by the remains of brickwork on the ground.

It has a large spoil tip, much of it probably dating from the 1890s railway works. The depth in the original survey was 240 ft (73.2 m) and two later surveys which measured from the then ground level to the point at which the shaft met the tunnel gave a depth of 237 ft (72.2 m).

Trevor Ellis

Figure 69 - Large spoil tips at Cote Pit, much of it dating from the railway works.

The next shaft site, higher up the western side, is Brun Clough, today's No.2 Shaft. This was heavily-used in the construction of the North railway tunnel and has a vast spoil heap mainly from this period. In 1817 the sub-committee investigating the introduction of a steam tug said *"Was Pulehoyles, Redbrook and Brunclough Pits uncovered we conceive that no great inconvenience would arise from the smoke of a small Steam Engine to haul Boats through this Tunnel"*, so the shaft seems to have been capped in some way after the completion of the Canal Tunnel. The pond, which remains today, is almost certainly a remnant of the water works for a water balance engine *(see Figure 76)* and the 1844 section mentions *"ruinous building formerly an engine house"*. In 1865 it had *"Field, Spoil Bank, Old Engine House, Pond, Footpath and Shaft"*, which by 1887 had become simply *"Pond, Old Dam, Ventilating Shaft"*, suggesting that tipping had covered the engine house. The shaft is thought to have been in progress prior to 1796, though its completion date is unclear. A new shaft close by was envisaged for the 1890s railway works, but had to be abandoned due to striking clay retaining a large quantity of water. A brick ring is visible, on the opposite side of the pond to the shaft and close to the footpath, marking the site of the infilled workings. Following the abandonment of this new shaft, the original canal shaft was enlarged to a diameter of 20 ft (6.1 m), at which time its depth was quoted as 457 ft (139.3 m). It is 1,742 yd (1592.9 m) from the present Diggle entrance and is not directly over the canal, being reached by a short adit. Once surrounded by a 10 ft (3.0 m) brick wall, at the end of the steam railway era this was lowered and the shaft capped in concrete. Arup did not survey it, presumably because of access problems due to the capping.

Examination of the extensive Redbrook site reveals a limited amount of spoil that can be linked to the canal and early railway works, on the downhill side of the engine house where the track approaches. The bulk of material is on the uphill side of the Engine House and clearly mostly tipped from the later Redbrook New shaft and thus the product of the final railway works. This later shaft was built between 1890 and 1892 and is a brick-lined shaft 18 ft (5.5 m) in diameter. Its depth was originally surveyed as 512 ft (156.1 m) but later quoted as

546 ft (166.4 m), which shows the depth of material which was tipped around it. Like Brun Clough, it is today capped in concrete and thus was not surveyed by Arup. It is today's No.3 Shaft, at a distance of 3,192 yd (2918.8 m) from the Diggle entrance. The foundations of a small building remain nearby.

Although it would appear that little of the Canal Tunnel was dug from Redbrook, the remains there are quite extensive. There are signs of extensive water management on Thieves Clough, just to the west of the tips, with a series of dams, the top one being linked to the main Redbrook Reservoir, on the far side of the present A62, by a channel following the contour. At the time of the canal works, a section of the first turnpike still continued the line of Mount Road, which now bends sharply to a T-junction with the A62, and dropped down to cross the stream before climbing up Thieves Clough on the East bank of the stream. It can still be traced and before the tips blocked the way, it would have given convenient access to the engine house.

A fragment of a map of the tunnels, which survives in the West Yorkshire Archives, dating from the construction of the second railway tunnel around 1865, shows another small reservoir to the west of the Redbrook Engine House, probably built for a water balance engine, but which also supplied water for a spray down one of the two shafts within the engine house to encourage ventilation, a practice which was maintained throughout the steam railway era. A later plan of 1897 shows a supply culverted under the tip which had by then covered the reservoir. This map also shows the additional buildings against the ends of the engine house, which once housed steam engines, and a separate range of buildings to the north, which correspond to *"Three Cottages Owned by the Huddersfield Canal Co."* on the 1844 section. These cottages are again listed on the 1887 plan, being *"Cottages, owned and occupied by the LNWR"*. Traces of the foundations may still be seen.

The engine house, as it stands, contains two shafts, mainly rock-cut, but apparently with some later brickwork lining. One of these shafts is over the Canal Tunnel, the 'Bye pit' or 'Upcast Shaft', while the 'Engine Pit' or 'Downcast Shaft' is offset to the South. They are today's No.4 and No.5 Shafts, at a distance of 3,292 yd (3010.2 m) from Diggle. It is thought that the reason why the 'Engine Pit' was offset was to avoid the pump rods from the engine and the sump for the pump obstructing the tunnel works. This 'Downcast' shaft contained the wooden trunking which allowed a spray of water down the shaft. The 'Upcast' shaft was measured at 140.0 m by Arup and the 'Downcast' at 146.0 m which suggests that they were measuring to the absolute bottoms as the latter shaft would have had the sump for the pumping engine. It is not known whether a water balance engine was ever actually installed at this site, as work never seems to have resumed after the departure of the original contractor.

The two Redbrook shafts were begun by 1796 and appear to have been complete by 1799, when tunnelling began in both directions, though progress was bedevilled by problems with contractors and in the 1806 report to the Annual Meeting *"107 yards complete and 50 yards headed"* were all that had been done. There is no evidence that this was ever extended by working from Redbrook, as the workings from the east were then close to meeting, and the tunnel's 'S-bend,' where a surveying error resulted in two lengths of tunnel failing to meet by 26 ft (7.9 m) is close to Redbrook on the west side. This suggests that the final length to be completed was driven from the western end towards Redbrook on a wrong alignment. The statement in 1808 about Redbrook that *"the levels were found to agree but the line differs"* was correct, in that the tunnel there is a few feet north of the true line, but an error of much greater magnitude than this resulted from the failure to accurately link up the two sections. It also appears odd that Redbrook, probably the hardest place in which to produce an accurate level, was correctly levelled when both ends were wrong - perhaps Redbrook was chosen as the 'true' level as it was between the levels at either end. It would certainly have been a massive undertaking to alter one of the ends by around five feet, which would have been the alternative. The nearby narrow section, to the east of the S-bend, which is the tightest section of the whole tunnel, may represent a late and hasty enlargement of the heading, described in the 1806 report, in an attempt to meet Telford's completion date. As at Brun Clough, the remarks of the sub-committee investigating steam towing in 1817 suggest that the shafts may have been covered at that time.

The original scheme for the Tunnel envisaged another shaft at Heathy Lee, 438 yd (400.5 m) east from Redbrook. This again was started by 1796 and was described as 'halfway' when work was suspended in 1799. Telford advised that it be abandoned. Today the water-filled top of the shaft may still be found *(Figure 8)*, with traces of a building, and this shaft and the bye pits for its drainage adit may be seen quite clearly on Google Earth® imagery.

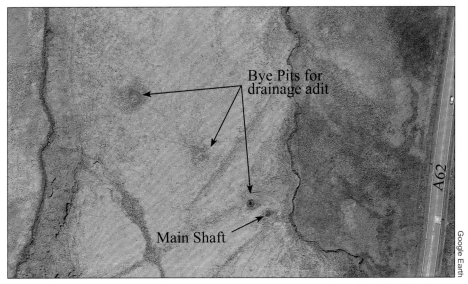

Figure 70 - A recent Google Earth® view of Standedge Moor showing the main shaft of Heathy Lee pit and its bye pits.

Continuing eastwards, the next shaft is Flint Pit, originally referred to as Pule Hoyles. This is the easiest to see from the road, being just above the present-day A62, though it would not have been quite so readily accessible when the Canal Tunnel was being built as this third turnpike over Standedge was not constructed until the 1830s. It was probably linked with the site at Gilberts, which was nearer to the first turnpike and where there are traces of cottages and other buildings. The shaft is situated 3,800 yd (3474.7 m) from Diggle and, like Heathy Lee, it was started by 1796 and about halfway to canal level when work was suspended due to the flood damage of 1799. However, Telford decided that it should continue to be worked, probably because it was midway between Pule and Redbrook, and it was completed by 1807. It still retains the remains of its engine house and the feed to the water engine can be seen as a narrow, level, reedy area of ground running from the direction of Gilberts and Redbrook Reservoir beyond. Within the engine house, water still runs from this feeder.

Figure 71 - A view across the A62 showing the feed to the water engine at Flint pit picked out by a break in the moorland vegetation.

As at Redbrook and Brun Clough, in 1817, the remarks of the sub-committee investigating the effect of a steam tug suggest that the Flint shaft may have been capped in some way. In July 1824, after the idea of a tug had been abandoned, the Committee minuted *"Resolved that Mr Raistrick be and hereby is empowered and directed to erect immediately an Arch in the Tunnel under Flint Pit and afterwards to fill up the said Pit"*, which seems to contradict this earlier statement.

It is known that a number of shafts were filled up, but whether Flint Pit (aka Pule Hoyles) shaft was, is open to question – as it stands today; it is open, but enlarged during later railway works. The 1844 section mentions the shaft, suggesting that this may be yet another example of a Minute that was never followed through, and an 'old canal reservoir,' which presumably had served a water engine. In the 1865 version it had 'Old Engine House, Spoil Bank, Land, Pond and Shafts', the plural 'shafts' suggesting that perhaps the other shaft(s) for the water balance engine may have then been open. Most sources agree that the old shaft is 10 ft (3.0 m) diameter. The original survey had it as 480 ft (146.3 m) deep, but later ones suggesting either 522 or 532 ft (159.1 or 162.2 m). Arups had it as 140.0 m deep and lined in brick and stone to 74.6 m.

Flint Pit was used again in the railway tunnel works and is another shaft which was enlarged and partly lined in brick in the 1890s, when Flint Pit New Shaft was also constructed close by, 3,938 yd (3600.9 m) from Diggle. The new shaft is either 16 or 18 ft (4.9 or 5.5 m) in diameter and its depth is quoted as 534 ft (162.8 m). For some reason, Arup did not survey the new shaft, though both shafts are open and surrounded by brick walls from the railway era. They are today numbered 6 and 7. Halfway between the shafts stands a concrete hut, with provision for a stove, which is probably the last monument to the soldiers who guarded the site in WW2.

The final shaft which remains open is Pule, No. 8 Shaft, which with its large spoil heap is visible above Tunnel End from Marsden. It was started around the same time as the other original shafts and was complete by 1799. It is sited 5142 yd (4701.8 m) from Diggle and has a depth originally estimated at 460 ft (140.2 m) and later quoted at 505 ft (153.9 m) which presumably represents the build-up of spoil. Arup gave it as 142.0 m, stating that 8.4 m were lined in stone and then brick to a depth of 49.2 m. In 1844 there were 'old canal reservoirs' nearby which had probably provided water for a water balance engine. It retains slight traces of what may have been an engine house and other buildings, but was enlarged to 12 ft (3.7 m) diameter in the later railway works. In 1865 it was described as 'Shaft, Spoil Bank, Waste Land and

Figure 72 - The bank of a small reservoir near Pule shaft supplying a water balance engine.

Trevor Ellis

Pond.' By 1887, there was no mention of the pond, but that plan does mention '*Building in Ruins.*' Unlike the other shafts it is surrounded by a square wall constructed in stone, of unknown date. The bank of a reservoir may be clearly seen a few yards to the South - Graham Keevil, in his '*Standedge Guide*' identified the sites of a series of small reservoirs.[99] On the tip side of the shaft is the concrete base of what may be another guard hut, which would certainly have been needed on a winter's night.

Pule Shaft was referred to at the time of building the Canal Tunnel as '*the Third Shaft on Pule*'. From Tunnel End it is possible to see the spoil heap of the second shaft, midway up the slope towards the much larger one at Pule. This shaft must have remained open for some time, as it is marked on a section prepared in 1844 as part of the plans for the first railway tunnel, where it is named as '*Old Canal Shaft*'. The first shaft would have been sited immediately above the third turnpike/ present day A62 and most traces will have been removed by the building and subsequent widening of that road. These two shafts were started immediately in 1794 and were probably complete by 1796.

◄●►

---

[99] *Keevil, G., (1986). Standedge Guide. (Kirklees Metropolitan Council)*

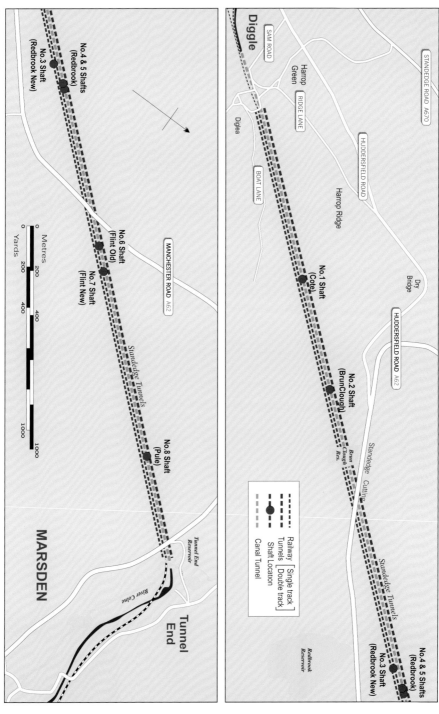

Figure 73 - Sketch map of the Standedge Tunnels from Diggle to Marsden locating the present day numbered shafts in use.

Annex 5
Methods

The Canal Tunnel was excavated by the mining techniques of the day and what references there are suggest that many of those looking to take on contracts were coal miners; a number of Welsh names are mentioned (Evans, Jenkins, Williams, Pritchard). The Tunnel was first driven as a heading or pilot tunnel at the level of the bottom of the finished Tunnel *(Figure 77a)*. Unlike later tunnelling practice, long lengths of heading seem to have been dug prior to enlargement. This may have been due to financial pressures or the need to reduce pumping costs by providing a means of draining the workings by gravity. As in coal mining, the heading was supported where necessary by wooden props and there are references in the Minutes to unexpected expenditure on timber when Outram's prediction that the Tunnel would be self-supporting proved incorrect. This also meant that far more of the Tunnel needed to be lined with stone arching after enlargement than he had predicted.

The available evidence suggests that blasting with gunpowder (Black Powder) was used to break up the rock and the marks of hand drills may still be seen on the harder rock sections. These would have been held by one man while another struck the end with a sledgehammer, the first man turning the drill each time to ensure that it did not stick. The traces remaining in the Tunnel's roof *(Figure 74)* are just the top row of what would have been multiple holes and the time taken to drill each hole in the harder millstone grit, working in near darkness, can only be imagined. This is why progress rates of only three feet per week were being achieved at the worst times and probably explains why a number of contractors gave up on the task.

There are references in connection with the shaft sinking to men lighting fuses and then being rapidly lifted up the shaft to what may or may not have been a safe distance before the charge fired. Accidents inevitably happened, both in the shafts and in the Tunnel, where practices would have been similar. When charges missed fire, it was down to the judgement of individuals how long to wait. The lack of sufficient ventilation would have been a constant problem as gunpowder creates a large amount of smoke.

Very early in the shaft sinking operations, there were references in the Minutes to obtaining coals and they mention trials with various types of coal to be delivered at Red Brook and Pule Hoyles. The steam engines which were in use were of the primitive Newcomen type. James Watt is often cited as being the inventor of the steam engine, but the Newcomen engine had first been introduced as early as 1712, if not before. Its drawback was that it used the force of atmospheric pressure to draw down a piston by condensing steam in a cylinder. The need to re-heat the cylinder at every stroke of the engine gave it a voracious appetite for coal. This had not been a great problem when the engine was used to drain coal mines, where coal was plentiful and the engines could burn the unsaleable 'small' coal, but on the moors at Standedge it would be a costly problem. Watt had improved the concept by

Ove Arup

Figure 74 - Marks of hand drills on a substantial block of Millstone Grit in Standedge Tunnel.

introducing a separate condenser, together with better engineering, which made his engine vastly more economical, but he had a Patent for 25 years and charged a premium for its use. Watt engines were considered by Outram in 1798, but he seems to have realised that the Committee would be unwilling to meet the cost.

Figure 75 - A postcard of a derelict Newcomen engine at Bardsley, Oldham, known as 'Fairbottom Bobs'. The card is mis-titled as Watt's first engine. The Newcomens on Standedge were erected in engine houses as illustrated in Figure 6. The layout of Beam and Cylinder would be the same.

Steam engines are definitely mentioned at Cote Pit, Brun Clough, Redbrook (where there was both a large and a small engine) and at Pule Hoyles/Flint Pit. One of the engines at Redbrook was probably a winding engine, though the Newcomen type of engine, with its jerky operation, was ill-suited to anything requiring rotary motion. At some of the lesser shafts, horse gins may have sufficed.

In February 1797 the Company were having trouble with the engines and the Minutes record *"Messrs Smith of Chesterfield having furnished the Huddersfield Canal Company with Pipes for the large Engine at Red Brook which on being put into Work have failed by defect of the Casting and caused considerable loss to the Company."* At the same meeting, there is a debate about *"the small engine"* which had also been supplied by Mr Smith of Chesterfield. There seems to have been a dispute about the suitability of the engine, which must have been partly justified as Smith had agreed to make modifications. He seems to have been guilty of supplying a smaller engine than that which had been ordered.

One reason for continuing with the primitive Newcomen-type engines may be that it was always the intention to use water power when and where possible, but this would only be when the necessary reservoirs and additional shafts and adits had been cut. The mention of the sale of the steam engine at Pule Hoyles/Flint Pit in February 1799 probably indicates the completion of the water system which can still be traced at this site. Water could be used in the form of water wheels, for pumping, or water balance engines for lifting. The latter required the digging of additional shafts both for the water bucket and to create a tunnel or sough to take the waste water to the nearest stream. As was normal practice in mining, soughs or adits were, in any case, dug at most of the shaft sites to reduce the amount of ground water, probably excluding the first two on Pule and two of those nearest to Diggle. These works are shown on the section drawn by Nicholas Brown around 1799 *(Figure 7)*.

We know from the deposited plans for the second railway tunnel that there were then *"old engine houses"* at most of the five shaft sites described along with the remains of water systems at some of them. The only one not mentioned as having an engine house being Pule, which did have a reservoir and where there, nevertheless, appear to be possible foundations visible today. That engine house may therefore have already been demolished by the 1840s.

The first railway tunnel used five of the shafts which had been used in building the Canal Tunnel, but first these were enlarged, starting in October 1845. The other major benefit from the amalgamation with the Canal Company was the ability to open adits to the Canal Tunnel at intervals and thus to create more working faces. Because of this method of working, with the new tunnel linked to the Canal Tunnel

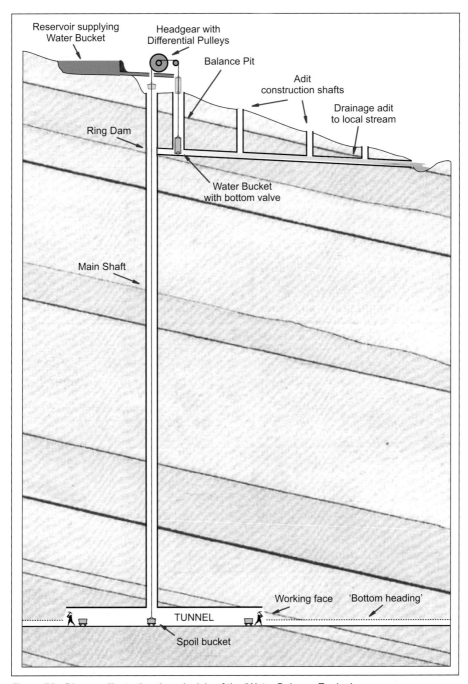

Figure 76 - Diagram illustrating the principle of the 'Water Balance Engine'.
(Bob Gough after Geoff Brown and R B Schofield)

which was at a lower level, it would seem likely that the first railway tunnel would have been bottom headed, but because of the number of working faces, the headings would have been enlarged relatively soon, rather than creating long lengths of heading as in the earlier Tunnel. 15 long and 4 short narrowboats were advertised for sale in April 1850 on completion of the works.

The other advantage of having the canal as part of the undertaking was that there was now a ready means of supply of fuel and steam power which could now be used without restriction. No less than five 25 horsepower (hp) engines were advertised in the sale, along with five sets of head gears, which suggests that one was erected at each shaft. These were high pressure engines, which would be vastly more economical than the type of engine in use on the earlier works. Another engine of 12 hp powered a mortar mill. 200 small wagons and no less than 30 turntables were included, giving an idea of the extent of the temporary railways used. The advertisement mentions that the wagons had been wound up the shafts, though some of the turntables would clearly have been used at the adits in order that wagons could be tipped into boats.

The second railway tunnel may have made even greater use of the Canal Tunnel, rather than the shafts, as there only appears one 25 hp engine in the various sale adverts and three or four lesser engines of 12, 8 and 5 hp with no mention of head gearing. The adits in this case needed to run beneath the earlier railway tunnel, but 24 open narrowboats and 4 screw steamboats are advertised, along with *"200 iron skips used in boats"*. *"A great number"* of tip wagons and *"several"* turntables are mentioned.

An interesting report appeared in the Huddersfield Examiner of 12th September 1868, which reported a drilling match between two tunnel workers and two quarrymen which gives an insight into their methods. The contest was to see which could drill a hole four feet in depth the quicker. Both were to use a *"2½ inch wall drill"*, the tunnel workers using an 8 lb hammer and the quarrymen either 16 lb or 28 lb, though

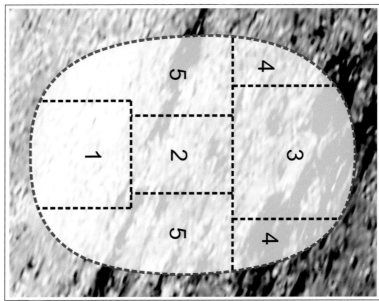

Figure 77a - A probable sequence of excavation of the 'bottom headed' Canal Tunnel. The 'heading' (1), at the bottom of the finished level, aids the disposal of the spoil from the subsequent excavation via a tramway to the nearest shaft.

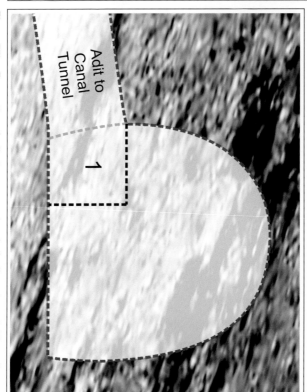

Figure 77b - Excavation of a 'bottom corner headed' railway tunnel. The railway tunnels were all constructed at a higher level than the Canal Tunnel, so connecting adits were constructed for the convenient disposal of spoil from the works.

the reason for the difference is not stated. After 1 hour and 25 minutes, the quarrymen won by about an inch, though it was said that the result would have been reversed had the tunnellers not broken their tools and had to have them repaired.

The Third tunnel was 'bottom corner headed' *(Figure 77b)*, linked by adits across to the First railway tunnel. Today, these are 'floored-in' by wooden bridges, but during the works there would presumably have been provision at each for tipping into boats. Only at one point, close to Brun Clough, is there a direct opening from the railway tunnel to the canal, which coincides with one of the 'wides'. The lack of information about the works in the published accounts is indicative of the decreasing public interest in civil engineering works, now that such things were an everyday occurrence.

Following the completion of this tunnel, there is no sign of a sale, which is probably due to the work being carried out 'in house' by the LNWR, who would have simply moved the equipment to another job.

It is interesting to note how tunnelling techniques changed during the period between the Canal Tunnel and the Third railway tunnel. Many tunnels are now bored by large tunnel boring machines, though blasting may still be used in hard rock areas. The biggest advances have been made in surveying, where the errors of many feet, which were a 'part and parcel' of the Canal Tunnel, have now been replaced by Global Positioning Systems (GPS) and errors are in millimetres, if at all.

However, even today, it is still amazing to look back on what was achieved with the primitive equipment of the time and to marvel at the persistence which brought that Tunnel to completion after around seventeen years.

ABBREVIATIONS

ACN	*Aire & Calder Naivgation Company*
BW	*British Waterways*
BWB	*British Waterways Board*
CRT	*Canal & River Trust*
DIWE	*Docks & Inland Waterways Executive*
HMRCC	*Huddersfield & Manchester Railway & Canal Company*
IWA	*Inland Waterways Association*
LMS	*London, Midland & Scottish Railway*
LNWR	*London & North Western Railway*
OS	*Ordnance Survey*
TA	*Territorial Army*
WW2	*World War 2*